30130087124987

STACK.

# A GUIDE TO THE BUTTERFLIES AND
# LARGER MOTHS OF ESSEX

# A Guide to the Butterflies and Larger Moths of Essex

*Compiled by a Panel consisting of:*

J. Firmin, MBOU (Chairman)

F. D. Buck          H. C. Huggins, FRES
A. J. Dewick        G. A. Pyman
D. G. Down          E. F. Williams, FRES

WATCH OVER
ESSEX

THE ESSEX NATURALISTS' TRUST

The Essex Naturalists' Trust Limited
Fingringhoe Wick
near Colchester
Essex

April 1975

ISBN 0 904768 00 7

Printed in Great Britain by
The Anchor Press Ltd
Tiptree, Essex

# Contents

ILLUSTRATIONS

# JOINT COMMITTEE FOR THE CONSERVATION
## OF BRITISH INSECTS

# A CODE

## FOR

# INSECT COLLECTING

# JOINT COMMITTEE FOR THE CONSERVATION OF BRITISH INSECTS

# A CODE FOR INSECT COLLECTING

This Committee believes that with the ever-increasing loss of habitats resulting from forestry, agriculture, and industrial, urban and recreational development, the point has been reached where a code for collecting should be considered in the interests of conservation of the British insect fauna, particularly macrolepidoptera. The Committee considers that in many areas this loss has gone so far that collecting, which at one time would have had a trivial effect, could now affect the survival in them of one or more species if continued without restraint.

The Committee also believes that by subscribing to a code of collecting, entomologists will show themselves to be a concerned and responsible body of naturalists who have a positive contribution to make to the cause of conservation. It asks all entomologists to accept the following Code in principle and to try to observe it in practice.

## I. COLLECTING—GENERAL

**1.1** No more specimens than are strictly required for any purpose should be killed.

**1.2** Readily identified insects should not be killed if the object is to 'look them over' for aberrations or other purposes: insects should be examined while alive and then released where they were captured.

**1.3** The same species should not be taken in numbers year after year from the same locality.

**1.4** Supposed or actual predators and parasites of insects should not be destroyed.

**1.5** When collecting leaf-mines, galls and seed heads never collect all that can be found; leave as many as possible to allow the population to recover.

**1.6** Consideration should be given to photography as an alternative to collecting, particularly in the case of butterflies.

**1.7** Specimens for exchange, or disposal to other collectors, should be taken sparingly or not at all.

**1.8** For commercial purposes insects should be either bred or obtained from old collections. Insect specimens should not be used for the manufacture of 'jewellery'.

## 2. COLLECTING—RARE AND ENDANGERED SPECIES

**2.1** Specimens of macrolepidoptera listed by this Committee (and published in the entomological journals) should be collected with the greatest restraint. As a guide, the Committee suggests that a pair of specimens is sufficient, but that those species in the greatest danger should not be collected at all. The list may be amended from time to time if this proves to be necessary.

**2.2** Specimens of distinct local forms of Macrolepidoptera, particularly butterflies, should likewise be collected with restraint.

**2.3** Collectors should attempt to break new ground rather than collect a local or rare species from a well-known and perhaps over-worked locality.

**2.4** Previously unknown localities for rare species should be brought to the attention of this Committee, which undertakes to inform other organisations as appropriate and only in the interests of conservation.

## 3. COLLECTING—LIGHTS AND LIGHT-TRAPS

**3.1** The 'catch' at light, particularly in a trap, should not be killed casually for subsequent examination.

**3.2** Live trapping, for instance in traps filled with egg-tray material, is the preferred method of collecting. Anaesthetics are harmful and should not be used.

**3.3** After examination of the catch the insects should be kept in cool, shady conditions and released away from the trap site at dusk. If this is not possible the insects should be released in long grass or other cover and not on lawns or bare surfaces.

**3.4** Unwanted insects should not be fed to fish or insectivorous birds and mammals.

**3.5** If a trap used for scientific purposes is found to be catching rare or local species unnecessarily it should be re-sited.

**3.6** Traps and lights should be sited with care so as not to annoy neighbours or cause confusion.

## 4. COLLECTING—PERMISSION AND CONDITIONS

**4.1** Always seek permission from landowner or occupier when collecting on private land.

**4.2** Always comply with any conditions laid down by the granting of permission to collect.

**4.3** When collecting on nature reserves, or sites of known interest to conservationists, supply a list of species collected to the appropriate authority.

**4.4** When collecting on nature reserves it is particularly important to observe the code suggested in section 5.

## 5.  COLLECTING—DAMAGE TO THE ENVIRONMENT

**5.1** Do as little damage to the environment as possible.   Remember the interests of other naturalists; be careful of nesting birds and vegetation, particularly rare plants.

**5.2** When 'beating' for lepidopterous larvae or other insects never thrash trees and bushes so that foliage and twigs are removed. A sharp jarring of branches is both less damaging and more effective.

**5.3** Coleopterists and others working dead timber should replace removed bark and worked material to the best of their ability. Not all the dead wood in a locality should be worked.

**5.4** Overturned stones and logs should be replaced in their original positions.

**5.5** Water weed and moss which has been worked for insects should be replaced in its appropriate habitat.   Plant material in litter heaps should be replaced and not scattered about.

**5.6** Twigs, small branches and foliage required as foodplants or because they are galled, e.g. by clearwings, should be removed neatly with secateurs or scissors and not broken off.

**5.7** 'Sugar' should not be applied so that it renders tree-trunks and other vegetation unnecessarily unsightly.

**5.8** Exercise particular care when working for rare species, e.g. by searching for larvae rather than beating for them.

**5.9** Remember the Country Code !

## 6.  BREEDING

**6.1** Breeding from a fertilised female or pairing in captivity is preferable to taking a series of specimens in the field.

**6.2** Never collect more larvae or other livestock than can be supported by the available supply of foodplant.

**6.3** Unwanted insects that have been reared should be released in the original locality, not just anywhere.

**6.4** Before attempting to establish new populations or 'reinforce' existing ones please consult this Committee.

Printed by Pendragon Press, Papworth Everard, Cambridge.

# Foreword

by JOHN F. CRITTALL, J.P., D.L.
*President of the Essex Naturalists' Trust*

Over 70 years have passed since the publication in the *Victoria County History of Essex* of the late W. H. Harwood's account of the county's butterflies and moths but up to now no revision of his list has been attempted.

The need for a new County Lepidoptera has, however, been obvious for a number of years. Since Harwood's day tremendous changes—most for the worse—have taken place in the Essex countryside, resulting in the loss of not a few species, particularly among our butterflies, and a decline in the numbers of many others. At the same time a few species have actually increased, some new ones have become established, and an impressive number of others are known to have wandered to the county. Consequently the present composition of the county's butterfly and moth fauna differs greatly from that at the turn of the century.

It is with much pleasure, therefore, that I write this foreword to *A Guide to the Butterflies and Larger Moths of Essex* which is being published by the Essex Naturalists' Trust and which I am sure will be enthusiastically received and widely consulted.

The Trust was fortunate indeed in securing the services of seven Essex entomologists as a Panel to see the project through. The Panel has worked with great enthusiasm to bring the work to fruition in the short space of four years and has sifted through something like 12,000 records which have been either extracted from the literature or made available by field workers.

The Chairman of the Panel, J. Firmin, is a former President of the Colchester and District Natural History Society, an agricultural and natural history journalist, and the authority on the Lepidoptera of a wide area around Colchester. He has also been responsible for the *Guide*'s Historical Survey. The Panel's Correspondent, G. A. Pyman, is Vice-Chairman of the Naturalists' Trust's Council and has long studied the Lepidoptera of central and east-central Essex. He has compiled the Systematic List and its Appendix giving pre-1925 species with help from other Panel members and, jointly with H. C. Huggins, has written the section dealing with the broad features of the county in relation to its Lepidoptera. I know that Mr. Huggins's vast experience has been of inestimable value to the Panel. One of the country's most distinguished lepidopterists, his knowledge of the subject generally as well as of the Lepidoptera of south Essex is unsurpassed and it is pleasing to record that, although he is now an octogenarian, his quite remarkable memory remains unimpaired.

F. D. Buck, who was a leading British coleopterist, the Secretary of the Trust's Scientific Committee and formerly Editor of the British Entomological Society's *Transactions*, gave the Panel the benefit of his professional expertise in the printing field until his sudden death in March 1975 which was such a great loss to entomology and the cause of nature conservation in Essex. A. J. Dewick, the operator of a powerful mercury vapour lamp at Bradwell-on-Sea since the 1940s, has contributed a wealth of data on immigration and vagrancy: it can, I think, be fairly claimed that his list of recorded vagrants from the continent and occasionally even further afield is unsurpassed in Britain. D. G. Down, a protégé of Mr. Huggins, lives near him in south-east Essex and, like him, has an extensive knowledge of the Lepidoptera of the southern part of the county. To complete the list, E. F. Williams, a former President of the Essex Field Club, who has recorded the Lepidoptera in the area around Brentwood over many years, has performed invaluable work extracting countless records from the literature.

It has been the Panel's declared intention to produce a new Macrolepidoptera of Essex which is based on sound scientific principles and yet makes interesting reading, so that it will be popular not only with serious lepidopterists, whether professional or amateur, but also with those whose interest in the subject is less intense. I have no doubt that it has succeeded in its aim and that a more attractively presented and informative local work on this subject has yet to be produced.

Certainly it demands a place on the bookshelves of all who have an interest, however slight, in the butterflies and moths of our county.

I am glad to know that the Panel is to continue in being and that its objectives will now be, first, to keep the status of the Macrolepidoptera species under constant review so that a revision of the present work can be prepared readily when the time seems opportune; and, secondly, to compile, with a view to eventual publication, a list of the Microlepidoptera of Essex, our knowledge of which, although still sparse in many areas of the county, is now growing steadily. I wish its members every success in their future work.

Park Hall,
Great Bardfield,
nr. Braintree,
Essex.
*December 1974*

8

# Historical Survey

Essex has played a prominent part in the recording and study of Lepidoptera since the 17th century when the celebrated John Ray of Black Notley, 'father' of British scientific natural history, compiled *Historia Insectorum*—the History of Insects.

Ray began collecting insects in 1690 and by that time he had already published several works on natural history. In the closing years of the 17th century he was living at Dewlands, Black Notley, in considerable poverty, remote from libraries and collections and from contact with friends and fellow workers.

Determined to press on with his studies despite poor health, Ray carefully described insects found hear his home or sent to him by friends. He had a set of chip boxes and breeding cages and his specimens were kept, meticulously numbered and documented, in store boxes.

Ray's daughter, Margaret, caught moths for him at dusk in the garden and Thomas Simson, who worked for the Ray family, scoured the local countryside for specimens.

There was great excitement in July 1695 when Ray was presented with a specimen of *Apatura iris* L. (the Purple Emperor) captured by a Mr. Courtman at Castle Hedingham. In the same month he was given an example of *Limenitis camilla* L. (the White Admiral) captured not far from Tollesbury by a Mr. Morton. Ray's descriptions of these butterfles were the first ever to be published.

Ray's notes for the History of Insects contain the first published descriptions of *Pararge aegeria* L. (the Speckled Wood), *Erynnis tages* L. (the Dingy Skipper) and *Callophrys rubi* L. (the Green Hairstreak).

John Ray died in January 1705 and the History of Insects was published five years later, edited by William Derham. Ray described 47 British butterflies, six of them new to science, as well as many previously unknown moth species.

During the early years of the 18th century a number of collectors visited Epping Forest and other Essex districts in search of Lepidoptera and these included members of the Aurelian Society, a group of enthusiasts which met at the Swan Tavern, Change Alley, London, to exchange information and examine their specimens.

Dr. Alan Maclean, a Colchester physician with an all-round interest in natural history, studied Lepidoptera in the first half of the 19th century.

Although he was better known as an ornithologist Dr. Maclean made a number of important observations of butterfly life histories. He successfully reared the Purple Emperor and the White Admiral and was the first naturalist to make a thorough study of the hibernation of the latter. He noted its protective habit of spinning up a hibernaculum from a honeysuckle leaf.

In Maclean's day the Purple Emperor had still not vanished from the woods around Colchester. He found eggs and larvae on sallow bushes in High Woods, Colchester, and also at Dedham and Langham, and he told friends of his pleasure in watching the male butterflies soaring round the tops of the oaks.

Miss Laetitia Jermyn, an Ipswich naturalist who wrote a charming little book entitled *The Butterfly Collector's Vade Mecum* in 1827, described a special butterfly net invented by Dr. Maclean.

She wrote in her instructions for collecting butterflies: 'Under this head may be mentioned a very ingenious net for taking butterflies invented by Doctor Maclean of Colchester, which may be called Maclean's Elastic Net. It is constructed of two pieces of stout split cane, connected by a joint at each end, and with a rod which lies between them, in which a pulley is fixed. Through this a cord fastened to the canes passes; a long cane with a ferrule receives the lower end of the rod and forms a handle; and to the cane is fastened a net of green gauze.'

Dr. Maclean died in 1869 but during his lifetime Essex had come to the forefront of Lepidoptera collecting through the activities of the famous Doubleday brothers, Henry and Edward, of Epping.

It may not be widely known that Essex is the home of the method of luring moths known as 'sugaring'. In fact it was Henry Doubleday who introduced the technique in the 1840s, thus revolutionising the whole field of moth collecting.

The Doubleday brothers kept a grocery shop in Epping High Street and it was Edward who first discovered that moths were attracted to sugar. In 1832 he was in the yard of the grocery warehouse one evening when he noticed a number of moths clustered on empty sugar barrels. Edward wrote to a naturalists' journal about his discovery recommending moth collectors 'simply to lay a hogshead of sugar which has just been emptied, in an open space near a garden or field'.

In 1841 Henry Doubleday tried the experiment of brushing a mixture of sugar and water on the bark of trees in Epping Forest. Success was immediate and many moths, some hitherto thought to be great rarities, were captured.

Soon other collectors began to smear their concoctions, based on sugar and treacle, on trees and fence posts. Dealers cashed in on the boom by advertising their own mixtures at fancy prices.

Those were the picturesque days of moth collecting when scissors

10

nets and clap nets were still in use and top-hatted entomologists in long jackets used bull's-eye lanterns to look for their quarry. One can imagine the excitement of those side-whiskered collectors as the light of their lanterns fell on the gleaming brown patches of sugar—and on some of the uncommon species they had attracted.

William H. Harwood, the Colchester entomologist and dealer, and author of the section on insects in the *Victoria County History*, used sugaring with great success. Harwood, born at Colchester in February 1840, was a true pioneer who has not received the recognition his painstaking work deserves.

Nowadays entomologists all over the world rear caterpillars in muslin sleeves or tubes placed over growing food-plants. But it is not generally appreciated that Harwood was the first man to perfect the method in the back garden of his home in North Station Road, Colchester.

For well over half a century, from the 1850s until his death in 1917, Harwood was a prominent figure in local and national natural history circles. By means of the sleeving method he was able to describe the life histories of many insects which had not previously been recorded.

He corresponded with the leading entomologists and zoologists of the period, including the celebrated Edward Newman and Richard South, both of whom used his records and notes when compiling standard works.

Harwood's name appears frequently in William Buckler's nine-volume masterpiece on the larvae of British butterflies and moths which was published by the Ray Society between 1885 and 1889.

As a small boy Harwood, who was educated at Colchester Royal Grammar School, spent much time roaming the woods and fields around Colchester hunting for birds, insects and plants. When he left school he was apprenticed to a firm of chemists but the work did not suit the young man, whose heart was set on becoming a professional naturalist.

Harwood was advised by his doctor to take up some form of outdoor work and he set up as a professional naturalist specialising in the collection and study of insects but also dealing in all kinds of natural history specimens.

Many of the butterflies and moths reared or collected by Harwood found their way into the collections of notable entomologists. The Hon. Charles Rothschild bought from him some unusual aberrations and varieties of Lepidoptera and some of these can be seen in the National Collection. A few of the most outstanding of these aberrations were figured in colour by F. W. Frohawk (see below) in his works on British butterflies.

During his searches for specimens Harwood spent countless days and nights in the Essex countryside. He knew every inch of High

11

Woods (Colchester), Donyland Woods and Friday Woods, and during the summer spent a good deal of his time in Weeley Woods, now largely destroyed, and the then famous collecting ground of Hartley Wood, St. Osyth.

In his notes on the entomology of the Colchester area, contained in *Benham's Guide to Colchester*, Harwood wrote that he had found 46 species of butterfly in that district.

Harwood planted *Silene otites* (the Breckland Catchfly) in the sandy crevices of the walls of Colchester Castle so that he could have a handy supply of this rare plant on which to rear larvae of the equally rare *Anepia irregularis* Hufn. (the Viper's Bugloss moth).

William Harwood died on Christmas Eve, 1917, and *The Entomologist* carried a full page obituary notice. His two sons also became well-known entomologists. They were Bernard Smith Harwood, who died in 1933, and Philip Harwood, who died in 1957. Philip Harwood, who lived for many years in Scotland, amassed one of the finest collections ever made of British insects. This collection, containing many of W. H. Harwood's specimens, was bequeathed to the British Museum.

The Victorian period produced many entomologists of great eminence. One of these was Paymaster-in-Chief Gervase Frederick Mathew, R.N. (Ret'd), whose name is perpetuated by *Leucania favicolor* Barr. (Mathew's Wainscot).

Mathew, who retired from the Royal Navy in 1902, discovered the moth which bears his name when collecting on the salt marshes at Dovercourt in July 1895. He was convinced that the wainscot moths he had found feeding on the flowering heads of marsh grasses were something new. He informed Charles Barrett, author of the monumental 11-volume work, *The Lepidoptera of the British Isles*, of his captures and submitted specimens, including varieties with reddish coloured forewings. In 1896 Barrett confirmed that the moths from the north Essex saltings were indeed a species new to Britain.

Mathew, who had joined the Royal Navy as a clerk in 1861 when he was 19, travelled extensively in the service and was able to study the Lepidoptera of the Mediterranean region and the Pacific zone as well as that of the British Isles. In 1886 he was posted to H.M.S. *Penelope* at Harwich and subsequently became District Paymaster to the Harwich Coastguard District. On his retirement to his home at Lee House, Dovercourt, he continued to devote himself to the collection and study of butterflies and moths. Rearing Mathew's Wainscot from egg to imago he painstakingly described every stage in its life history in *The Entomologist's Monthly Magazine* in 1905. He also reared from north Essex stock a remarkable strain of *Arctia villica* L. (the Cream-spot Tiger) with greatly enlarged spots on the forewings.

Stour Woods, Wrabness, were a happy hunting ground for Mathew and in his day the Purple Emperor could still be found there: one of Mathew's specimens of this fine insect is in the Colchester Natural History Museum collection.

Mathew died at Dovercourt on the eve of his 86th birthday, on 10 February 1928. But until his final illness he had remained remarkably alert and active, collecting in the local woods and marshes and contributing notes to entomological journals. Between 1855 and 1925 he wrote more than 300 papers and notes, mainly on Lepidoptera. At his death he shared the distinction with the Rev. A. E. Eaton of being senior Fellow of the Royal Entomological Society. Most of the veteran entomologist's specimens went either to the British Museum or to the Hope Department, Oxford.

Contemporaries of Mathew were E. A. Fitch and the Rev. G. H. Raynor who between them added vastly to the knowledge of the butterflies and moths of east-central Essex.

Fitch, an all-round naturalist, was a native of Maldon and recorded diligently in and around that small market town at the head of the Blackwater estuary, while Raynor, for many years the incumbent at Hazeleigh to the south-west of Maldon, spent countless hours familiarising himself with the Lepidoptera of that parish and the country westwards towards Chelmsford, including Danbury Ridge. He also made an intensive study of the aberrations of *Abraxas grossulariata* L. (the Magpie moth). Both men published comprehensive local lists in *The Essex Naturalist*, to which, incidentally, Professor R. Meldola had contributed an equally valuable and exhaustive list of Epping Forest Lepidoptera some years earlier.

Probably the greatest scientific entomologist Essex has so far produced was the Rev. Charles R. N. Burrows who was Vicar of Mucking for 35 years after his appointment in 1897.

Burrows was a man of considerable intellect, and a painstaking natural scientist who encouraged the younger generation of entomologists to undertake serious studies. He was a friend and associate of the famous J. W. Tutt, founder of *The Entomologist's Record*. Papers by Burrows on the emerald group of moths and on a number of noctuid moth species appeared in that journal.

Probably the most important research conducted by Burrows, in collaboration with F. N. Pierce, was in the field of species determination through the scientific dissection of genitalia. He unravelled the confusion surrounding the *Hydraecia* group of moths and detected a new species, *Hydraecia crinanensis* Burrows (the Crinan Ear). Burrows' paper 'On the *nictitans* group of the genus *Hydraecia* Guen.' appeared in the *Transactions* of the Royal Entomological Society in 1911.

Later Burrows worked on the Psychid group and published a number of papers on his work. Before his death in 1932 he presented his Psychid specimens to the British Museum.

Another entomologist who was actively collecting and studying

Lepidoptera in Essex in the early years of the century was F. G. Whittle of Shoebury. His collection was likewise left to the British Museum. Whittle, like Burrows, approached his work from a scientific angle and it is thanks to him that the Lepidoptera of Southend-on-Sea and district in the early 1900s is so well documented.

The distinguished author and artist Frederick William Frohawk lived in Essex for a total of 15 years and during this time carried out many of the butterfly life history studies described and illustrated in *The Natural History of British Butterflies* and, later, in *The Complete Book of British Butterflies*. There are frequent references in Frohawk's books to Essex.

Frohawk, who died in 1946, lived at Ashmount, Rayleigh, from *c*. 1900 to *c*. 1910 and at Uplands, Thundersley, from 1918 to 1923. While at Thundersley he found a large number of butterfly species in or near his garden and was able to use some of these as subjects for his beautiful paintings.

Essex has given its name to two species of Lepidoptera—*Adopoea lineola* Ochs. (the Essex Skipper) and *Thetidia smaragdaria* F. (the Essex Emerald).

The Essex Skipper has a particularly interesting history. It was not known as British before 1889, when three specimens captured by F. W. Hawes at Hartley Wood, St. Osyth, were identified as a separate species instead of aberrations of *Adopoea sylvestris* Poda (the Small Skipper). Mr. Hawes noticed that the butterflies were slightly different from the Small Skipper with which they were flying. The tips of their antennae were entirely black, instead of black above and orange-red underneath as in the Small Skipper and there were other minor, but significant, differences.

The capture of these specimens at St. Osyth was recorded in *The Entomologist* in 1890 and there was an immediate investigation of series of Small Skippers in collections. It was found that a number of skippers labelled as Small Skippers were, in fact, Essex Skippers.

F. W. Frohawk found three specimens of *lineola* in his cabinet which had been collected in Norfolk early in the last century. Searches were made throughout Essex and it was soon clear that the new species, which had been separated on the continent many years previously, was locally abundant in Essex, Suffolk and other eastern and southern seaboard counties.

The first specimen of the Essex Emerald noticed in Britain was recorded by W. Curtis in *British Entomology*. Curtis wrote that a specimen 'was reared from a larva found by Mr. Parsons at Southchurch, Essex, in the year 1826'.

In 1845 five specimens were captured by J. W. Douglas at St. Osyth among grass on a sea wall. These specimens went to the collection of Dr. P. B. Mason of Burton-on-Trent.

In the 1800s London collectors searched systematically for Essex

Emerald larvae among sea-wormwood plants near the estuaries of the Rivers Blackwater, Crouch and Thames and found the species to be widespread and in good numbers. Since then this beautiful insect which bears our county's name has become extremely restricted and scarce and must now be considered one of Britain's most localised moths, suffering severely from habitat changes, herbicide sprays which destroy its food-plant, and the effects of pollution on its maritime haunts. It may be added that the activities of some collectors have also contributed to its decline.

# The Broad Features
# of the County

The recording area for this Guide is the geographical county of Essex which includes that part of the Metropolis which lies to the north of the River Thames and east of the River Lea.

The area of 'geographical' Essex is 1,528 square miles. It is bounded on the south by the Thames estuary and river, on the west by the Rivers Lea and Stort, on the north by the Stour estuary and river, and on the east by the North Sea. Sand and gravel deposits are to be found locally in some river flood-plains and also on certain hill features and near the coast; but most of the county consists of clay—London clay in the south and boulder clay in the north. Frequent chalk outcrops are to be found on the boulder clay towards the north-west and there are others (though mostly built over) along Thames-side in the Grays-Purfleet area. Eastwards towards the coast and estuaries the terrain becomes flat and marshy but inland there are a number of low hill features and the country is much diversified with woodlands, fields, meadows and a few areas of heathland. The river valleys and the many artificially created waters complete the picture.

The coast and estuaries of Essex are of considerable importance from the entomological standpoint. There are no less than 300 miles of sea-wall, extending from the head of the Stour estuary round to the Port of London on the Thames estuary, and the estuaries and inlets contain a number of islands, some of them large like Horsey Island in Hamford Water and Foulness.

On the seaward side of the sea-wall are to be found the saltings, the home of *Malacosoma castrensis* L. (the Ground Lackey) and *Thetidia smaragdaria* F. (the Essex Emerald) which are confined to the coast of south-east England (the latter possibly now solely to Essex), although on the continent they occur inland. Here, too, the shingle and shell beaches (the 'coast sands' of the old authors) are located, Walton Naze, Colne Point (now an Essex Naturalists' Trust reserve) and Bradwell being the most important. They are the haunt of a number of specialised species such as *Agrotis vestigialis* Hufn. (the Archer's Dart), *Agrotis ripae* Hübn. (the Sand Dart) and *Heliophobus albicolon* Hübn. (the White Colon), while there and elsewhere round the littoral occur other localised insects, *Leucania favicolor* Barr. (Mathew's Wainscot), *Apamea oblonga* Haw. (the Crescent Striped) and *Hydraecia paludis* Tutt (the Saltern Ear) among them.

The growth on the sea-wall extending to the drainage dykes on its landward side contains numerous colonies of *Polyommatus icarus* Rott. (the Common Blue) and *Adopoea lineola* Ochs. (the Essex Skipper) as well as *Aspitates ochrearia* Rossi (the Yellow Belle) and *Scopula promutata* Guen. (the Mullein Wave), and the uncultivated ground along the coastal strip is the haunt of *Arctia villica* L. (the Cream-spot Tiger) and *Saturnia pavonia* L. (the Emperor moth) among a number of other species.

Inland of the sea-wall lie the fresh-water marshes which unhappily have been intensively drained of late, but which still contain in places fairly extensive reed-beds, the haunt of numerous members of the large wainscot family of moths as well as other species which feed on aquatic vegetation.

The inland waters of Essex comprise the rivers and streams with their marshes—now reduced by drainage and ploughing to a pitiful remnant—together with the artificial lakes (Birch, Gosfield, etc.), reservoirs (notably Abberton and Hanningfield) and flooded gravel-pits. Waters in the latter two categories have much increased in number in recent years and for many but by no means all 'aquatic' species have provided replacements for the lost breeding grounds along the river valleys. They have even added new moth species to the Essex list: in one flooded gravel-pit which became worked out only 40 years ago, three species new to the county list were found in the late 1950s. In addition to the wainscots such localised moths as *Apamea unanimis* Hübn. (the Small Clouded Brindle) and *Apamea ophiogramma* Esp. (the Double-lobed) are to be found in these damp situations.

In earlier times large tracts of the Essex countryside away from the coastal fringe were wooded but today only some 45 square miles of forest, wood and spinney remain. Situated mostly in the southern half of the county the principal surviving woodland belts are Epping and Hatfield Forests and the woods round Brentwood (including the extensive South Weald and Thorndon country parks); near Ongar; in the Margaretting/Ingatestone/Blackmore area; on Langdon Hills and Danbury Ridge; in the Hockley and Hadleigh districts; and along the Roman River valley south of Colchester.

There are, however, some quite large and scientifically important woods remaining in the northern part of the county: Chalkney Wood (Earls Colne) and Hempstead Wood are good examples, the latter being one of a number situated on the boulder clay towards the north-west where the ash is the predominant tree. To the south and east oak and hornbeam come into their own and in some woods there is a great diversity of timber. In recent years much replanting with conifers has taken place, more in the north than in the south of the county, and although the number of species is thereby diminished it has already resulted in the appearance, or extension of range, of several species associated with conifers which had previously been absent from, or extremely local in, Essex: an example in the first category is *Thera variata* Schiff. (the Grey Spruce Carpet) and in the latter, *Panolis flammea* Schiff. (the Pine Beauty).

The larger (and some smaller) woods were until comparatively recently the haunt of several species of fritillary butterflies, *Limenitis camilla* L. (the White Admiral) and *Apatura iris* L. (the Purple Emperor), but today all appear to have vanished except that *Argynnis aglaia* L. (the Dark Green Fritillary) is still seen occasionally in south Essex and the White Admiral clings precariously to a few woods in the south and south-east. But it is some consolation to know that *Pararge aegeria* L. (the Speckled Wood), which reappeared in Essex 20 years ago after a virtual absence of half a century, is now fairly widespread in the southern half of the county and still extending its range.

The number of species of the larger moths to be found in our woods and well-timbered parks is still impressive, however, and it is by no means rare to record 70–80 species on a favourable midsummer night in some woods containing an extensive variety of trees and flowering plants. Several species seem to have disappeared during the last quarter of a century including *Lymantria monacha* L. (the Black Arches) and *Boarmia roboraria* Schiff. (the Great Oak Beauty) but the great majority of our Essex woodland moths are still with us, even if some are less numerous and more localised than at the turn of the century. Any short selection of the more notable species from among such a large assemblage can only be arbitrary but we may mention *Stauropus fagi* L. and *Notodonta trepida* Esp. (the Lobster and Great Prominents), *Drymonia dodonea* Schiff. (the Light Marbled Brown), the delightful *Miltochrista miniata* Forst. (the Rosy Footman), the delicately-hued *Amathes glareosa* Esp. (the Autumnal Rustic), *Griposia aprilina* L. (the Merveille-du-Jour) and, among the geometers, *Geometra papilionaria* L. (the Large Emerald) and *Mesoleuca albicillata* L. and *Lampropteryx suffumata* Schiff. (the Beautiful and Water Carpets).

The heathlands of Essex have never been really extensive and today little is left of them. The principal areas are the Ministry of Defence lands south of Colchester, the commons on Danbury Ridge, and parts of Epping Forest. Heather, the food-plant of a number of heathland moths, is now to be found in any quantity (and then not extensively) only on Tiptree Heath and Danbury Ridge, in a locality south of Brentwood and in Epping Forest. With the decline of the heather some of the species associated with this plant have disappeared from the county but a few others, e.g. *Cybosia mesomella* L. (the Four-dotted Footman) and *Lycophotia varia* Vill. (the True Lover's Knot), still persist. Among other species associated in Essex with heathland but not reliant on heather may be mentioned *Eumenis semele* L. (the Grayling) which is found only round Colchester and is at present practically confined to the Ministry of Defence lands; the very localised *Hapalotis venustula* (the Rosy Marbled); and *Ortholitha plumbaria* F. (the July Lead-belle) which is now rare in the county.

Some 70 per cent of the total area of the county is now given up to agriculture. Today most of this land is arable, the remainder being divided between dairy and sheep farmland (now much decreased) and orchards. Over large tracts of Essex farmland, insect populations have been decimated in recent years by crop-spraying, stubble burning and the wholesale grubbing out of hedgerows and field-corner thickets. Moth species whose larvae feed on either hawthorn or blackthorn are among those which have suffered, an example being that very localised insect, *Bapta distinctata* H.-S. (the Sloe Carpet).

As previously mentioned there are two 'chalk' districts in Essex. One is the chalky boulder clay region in the north of the county and particularly in the north-west. This area has been little worked in recent years but some interesting discoveries have been made and others will no doubt follow. Two such discoveries, in the 1950s, are those of *Aegeria andrenaeformis* Lasp. (the Orange-tailed Clearwing), the first Essex record, and *Eupithecia pimpinellata* Hübn. (the Pimpinel Pug), both in the Saffron Walden area. There seems no reason to doubt old records from the same district of three species of chalk-loving 'blue' butterflies or of *Hesperia comma* L. (the Silver-spotted Skipper) in the days when these uplands were less intensively farmed than they are today.

The other district containing chalk is on Thames-side in the neighbourhood of Grays. Sadly, it is now much built-over or excavated for chalk, but the chalk form of *Plebejus argus* L. subsp. *cretacea* Tutt (the Silver-studded Blue) maintained a precarious existence there until about 1960 and *Ortholitha bipunctaria* Schiff. (the Chalk Carpet) has recently been recorded. Such chalk-haunting species as *Lophopteryx cucullina* Schiff. (the Maple Prominent) and *Xanthorhoe quadrifasiata* Clerck (the Large Twin-spot Carpet) are to be found here too, although they also occur, very locally and at low density, elsewhere in the county.

Gardens are playing an increasingly important part in the fortunes of our Essex Lepidoptera. As more and more houses are built so the number of gardens increases, and they provide for not a few species the sustenance denied them in the intensively farmed and often hedgerow-less open country. Some moths are, perforce, confined to gardens (and nurseries) as their food plants grow nowhere else: examples are *Hadena compta* Schiff. (the Varied Coronet) which arrived in Essex from the Kent coast in the early 1950s and feeds in this country on Sweet William; and *Rheumaptera cervinalis* Scop. (the Scarce Tissue) which relies for its continued existence on cultivated *Berberis*. Even the smallest suburban garden can boast a fair number of species and large, well-timbered ones in rural areas can harbour a great variety. *Eupithecia intricata* Zett., subsp. *arceuthata* Freyer (Freyer's Pug) is extending its range in the county, thanks to the increase in ornamental conifers; and the annual appearance in some numbers of *Eupithecia sobrinata* Hübn. (the Juniper Pug) in a garden on Danbury Ridge must surely result from the planting of ornamental juniper or some closely-related shrub in the vicinity.

This brief survey would not be complete without a reference to the 'concrete jungle'—the densely built-up areas in the Metropolitan part of Essex and in the centres of large towns. It might be thought that such places would be almost devoid of Lepidoptera but this is not the case. Whilst, obviously, the number of species is not high and their density is usually low, it is surprising what can be found. There are, for example, a number of records of *Mimas tiliae* L. (the Lime Hawk) in town centres where lime trees line the squares or pavements, and *Lycia hirtaria* Clerck (the Brindled Beauty) is another well-known town dweller. *Euclidia mi* Clerck (Mother Shipton) was recently discovered on waste land at Plaistow in east London and an example of *Pseudoips bicolorana* Fuessl. (the Scarce Silver-lines), an oak woodland species, was found a few years ago in Newham.

Reference has already been made to a number of changes in land management which are adversely affecting our Lepidoptera. In concluding this summary we would mention another phenomenon—the present-day mania for 'tidiness'. Throughout the county dead or diseased trees are being felled, as a direct result of which *Cossus cossus* L. (the Goat moth) is now almost a rarity; road-side verges are cut all too frequently so that the butterflies which used to abound in these flowery places are no longer a feature of them; and large areas of our public open spaces have been transformed into gigantic lawns, so regularly are they mown, with the result that those species of extensive rough grassland, *Macrothylacia rubi* L. (the Fox moth) among them, which formerly flew there in numbers, are now becoming scarce. Happily an increasing number of public bodies now recognise the ecological damage which such practices cause and a reversal of these policies is already apparent in some districts.

# Systematic List

The systematic list forms the main part of this work. It gives the status, with individual records in a number of cases, of all species of Macrolepidoptera—the butterflies and larger moths—which have been recorded in Essex over the past half century, i.e. back to and including 1925.

Those species which the Panel accepts as having occurred in the county before 1925, but of which there has since been no trace, are listed in the Appendix at the end of the list with brief notes on their former status or appearances.

The list follows the late I. R. P. Heslop's revised indexed *Check-List of the British Lepidoptera* (1964, with subsequent additions) except that the families *Syntomidae* and *Psychidae*, comprising a total of 28 British species, have been omitted as they were formerly included in the Microlepidoptera (see below) and are still widely treated as such.

It should be stressed that Heslop's choice of vernacular names has not been generally adopted for the list: occasionally, where it has been felt that a revised name is both an improvement and not so different from the old as to confuse those who rely on English nomenclature it has been used; but in the vast majority of cases the old name has been retained.

Much thought has been given during the planning of this guide as to whether the Microlepidoptera, of which there are nearly 1,500 species on the British list, should be included. But it was realised that our present knowledge of Essex species is still strictly limited, and that status summaries would be so incomplete that their publication could not be justified. Indeed, it is highly likely that a number of species still await discovery in the county.

Progressively more work is being carried out in Essex on this, the largest component of our Lepidoptera, and it is hoped in due course either to include these species in a revision of the present work or to make them the subject of a separate publication.

As the distribution trends of Essex butterflies have been more thoroughly documented over the years than those of moths, and as many people have a greater interest in butterflies than moths which are generally known by relatively few conspicuous species, the butterflies have, by and large, received fuller treatment in the list. This applies particularly to those species whose status and distribution have altered drastically during the past half-century.

While, clearly, the Panel cannot claim infallibility, it has gone to considerable lengths to satisfy itself as to the authenticity of all records mentioned in the list. In the case of rarities, or semi-rare or very local 'difficult' species, either the specimen has been examined or the Panel has assessed the admissibility of the record in the light of all available evidence. In all probability this has resulted in the omission of a few 'good' records but it has been felt that where the slightest doubt attaches to a record it is better not to publish it.

The Panel has admitted to the systematic list a total of no fewer than 635 species, almost two-thirds of the total number on the British list of Macrolepidoptera. When those pre-1925 species in the Appendix are added, it will be seen that the number of species reliably recorded in the county is 690.

By any standards this is an impressive total which few counties can surpass. To some extent it refutes the widely held view that Essex is not a 'good' county for Lepidoptera. It has to be appreciated, however, that a substantial number of the species occur at a markedly lower density in Essex than in those counties whose countryside has been relatively undisturbed. It should also not be overlooked that a significant proportion of the total comprises immigrants that have occurred over the years on or near the coast, especially at the large and powerful light trap which A. J. Dewick has long operated at Bradwell-on-Sea.

A study of the systematic list will soon show that many species of Essex butterfles and moths have declined materially—some catastrophically—in numbers this century and particularly since the second world war. A few have almost certainly become extinct in the county. In most cases the decline—or eclipse—is attributable to the destruction or major disturbance of the environment by man which unfortunately in Essex has been particularly marked of late years. On the other hand quite a few species have actually increased since the turn of the century due mainly to the spread of their foodplant, notably as a result of the creation of man-made habitats, e.g., reservoirs, and several others have colonised the county. Consequently the total number of *species* to be found in Essex today is probably little different from that of 50 years ago.

So far as the recording of our Macrolepidoptera is concerned, coverage is probably wider at the present time than it has ever been, but as a glance at the systematic list and the map will show it is still decidedly patchy. Nevertheless it can probably be claimed that in no other county is the present county-wide status of the various species better known. Among those localities which have received scant attention in recent years we should mention especially Epping Forest. Once worked extensively and noted for the richness of its Lepidoptera this important area has been seriously neglected of late and we do not know the present-day status of a number of its important species

22

or, indeed, whether some of them still exist there. However, it is encouraging to know that the recently established Epping Forest Conservation Centre has begun a survey of the Forest's Lepidoptera. Several useful records have been received from this source during 1974 and we can look forward to up-dating the information on a number of Epping Forest species in a future revision of this *Guide*.

It goes without saying that the Panel would be glad to hear of any errors in or omissions from the list. Now that a much needed yard-stick for the status of our Macrolepidoptera exists in the form of this *Guide*, it intends to keep the status of Essex butterflies and moths under frequent review. Any amendments notified will be filed for future publication.

In a number of cases the Panel has found it necessary to reject previously published records of rare or extremely local species, either because it is satisfied that a mistake or misunderstanding has occurred, or because, in its view, a genuine doubt exists in the light of know-ledge since acquired as to the record's validity. Where such records appear they have been placed in brackets.

In order to save space, where such records have been published in *The Essex Naturalist*, from which a substantial amount of material has been extracted, no reference is made in the list to their rejection. Their omission from the list can therefore be taken as intentional. The same remarks apply to the odd records located in the pages of non-scientific books or magazines.

Where no doubt attaches to a record, previously published or otherwise, but the *origin* of the specimen is regarded as suspect, the record has been placed in *square* brackets.

In compiling the systematic list the Panel has borne in mind constantly the need to exercise great care in not disclosing precise localities for rare or very local species: indeed, in the case of certain species whose position is especially precarious, it has felt fully justi-fied in withholding even a broad indication of the localities in which they are to be found as well as the recorders' names.

It has been found convenient as well as space-saving to refer to the following well-worked districts, each extending over several parishes and comprising what is basically a single physical feature, by the terms indicated:

Hamford Water
The shores of the large tidal inlet known as Hamford Water
    but excluding Dovercourt and The Naze

Dengie Peninsula
The marshes and farmlands east of a line running north
    from Burnham-on-Crouch to the Blackwater Estuary

Danbury Ridge
The woodland and commons in the parishes of Danbury,
Little Baddow and Woodham Walter, including seven
Essex Naturalists' Trust's nature reserves

Thames-side
The marshes, fleets, gravel-pits and uncultivated ground
along Thames-side between Fobbing and East Tilbury

The area frequently referred to in the list as the Rochford Hundred
comprises the lands between the Crouch and Thames estuaries
which extend from Foulness Point in the east to Rayleigh and South
Benfleet in the west.

The abbreviation 'Writtle Ag. Coll. coll.' refers to the collection
based at Writtle Agricultural College (formerly the Essex Institute
of Agriculture). The initials 'N.R.' stand for Nature Reserve of which
there are now nearly 40 in Essex, most of them owned or managed
by the Essex Naturalists' Trust.

Inevitably a number of references are made in the list to the last
check-list of Essex Macrolepidoptera, namely that compiled by the
late William H. Harwood for *The Victoria County History of Essex*
(1903) and these references are denoted by the initials 'VCH'.

The Panel expresses its grateful thanks to R. P. Hull for drawing
the map as well as the cover illustration of the Essex Emerald moth
and its larva; to G. B. Royffé for his photograph of S. J. Dewick's
M.V. trap; to Keith Huggett for the photographs of the Strood
Saltings, West Mersea, and Colne Point NR; to M. Skelton of the
Biological Records Centre, Monks Wood, and Mrs. J. Nicklen of
Rothamsted Experimental Station, Harpenden, for placing at its
disposal Essex records in their possession; to D. S. Fletcher of the
British Museum (Natural History) for checking specimens; to Dr.
C. G. M. de Worms for much assistance with records for the Metro-
politan part of Essex and for other help; to Mr. and Mrs. M. G.
Harrison for typing the fair copy of the systematic list; to the late
F. D. Buck, J. Heath (Colchester Natural History Museum), R. Tomlinson and E. F. Williams for extracting many records from the literature; and last but certainly not least to all those who have contributed records without which this *Guide* would have been a non-starter.

## RHOPALOCERA (BUTTERFLIES)

*Papilio machaon* L. (Swallowtail)
Rare immigrant: none seen since 1950. Reported since 1925
(singly, except once) from Benfleet and Canvey Island in July 1935
and Wakering in July 1936 (HCH); Bradwell-on-Sea on 16 July
and 1 August 1945 (*Entomologist*, 50:231) and 6 June 1950 (*Essex
Nat.*, 28:293); and Canvey Island on 7 August 1950 (*Essex Nat.*,

29:46): those examined belonged to the continental race *bigenerata* Verity. Specimens of the British subspecies *britannicus* Seitz found inland at Colchester in July 1938 (JF) and in 1947 (ADB) are thought to have been introduced locally.

*Pieris brassicae* L. (Large Garden White)
Still very common but far less abundant than formerly. Numbers are frequently augmented in late summer by immigrants.

*Pieris rapae* L. (Small Garden White)
As for preceding species.

*Pieris napi* L. (Green-veined White)
Still common, but markedly less so than formerly.

*Pontia daplidice* L. (Bath White)
Very rare immigrant. Comparatively recent records (all of individuals) are confined to three in the Southend-on-Sea area, viz. Shopland, 26 August 1935 (*Entomologist*, 69:55); Thorpe Bay, 24 August 1939 (*Entomologist*, 72:227); and Westcliff-on-Sea, 9 July 1947 (*Entomologist*, 80:193).

*Anthocaris cardamines* L. (Orange Tip)
Generally distributed and usually common, but numbers fluctuate markedly from year to year. Undoubtedly less numerous than formerly. A specimen of the yellow-tipped aberration, *aureoflavescens* Cockerell, was taken at Berechurch near Colchester on 18 May 1958 (JF).

*Colias hyale* L. (Pale Clouded Yellow)
Immigrant, currently scarce. Recorded almost annually but scarce and irregular since 1951, the last year of a seven-year period during which it was common on the coast, especially in the Dengie Peninsula (AJD). Ever since records began to be kept the years of plenty have been separated by lengthy periods during which the species has been scarce or even absent, but the present period of scarcity is already the longest known. In view of the decline of our immigrant butterflies generally there is a real fear that *C. hyale* will not again be seen in Essex in the numbers recorded in peak years of the past. Always relatively scarce inland, since 1951 it has been recorded away from the coast and estuaries only at Copford near Colchester on 4 September 1952 (JF) and near Upminster on 2 September (3) (RRC) and 5 September 1964 (*Ent. Rec.*, 76:243).

[*Colias australis* Verity (Berger's Clouded Yellow)
The specimen from 'Tillingbourne' (=Tillingham) exhibited to the South London Entomological and Natural History Society on 14 April 1948 (*Proc. S. Lond. ent. nat. Hist. Soc.*, 1948–9:5; *Entomologist*, 81:176) had in fact been reared by AJD from ova obtained at Folkestone, Kent. There is no indication that *C. australis* has occurred in Essex.]

*Colias croceus* Fourc. (Clouded Yellow)
Annual immigrant. Formerly it appeared in good numbers every

few years and was periodically abundant—e.g. 1,075 at Bradwell-on-Sea in 1949 (AJD)—but since 1952 it has been seen in no more than moderate numbers (in 1957 and 1967) and has usually been scarce or very scarce, with most records referring to the littoral and its vicinity, notably the Dengie Peninsula. Aberration *helice* Hübn. has been recorded frequently. A contributory factor in the decline of both this species and *C. hyale* above is undoubtedly the very marked reduction in the number of lucerne fields.

*Gonepteryx rhamni* L. (Brimstone)
Widely distributed, being absent only from extensive built-over areas and the more exposed parts of the coast, to both of which it occasionally wanders. Generally it occurs at low density, but it is fairly common, and in some years numerous, in extensively wooded districts, notably Danbury Ridge (GAP).

*Danaus plexippus* L. (Milkweed)
Very rare vagrant. There are but two fully authenticated Essex records of this, the Milkweed or Monarch, the largest butterfly on the British list. Two flew off a ship in Tilbury Docks in 1920 (*Entomologist*, 54:145) and one was seen at Leigh-on-Sea in mid-October 1968 (Mrs. E. Ballard *per* JFB). The latter was the year which saw an unparalleled arrival of this North American species, resulting in over 60 being seen in the British Isles. *D. plexippus* breeds in the USA and Canada and has established colonies in the Azores and the Canary Islands. The fact that the 1968 immigration coincided with an unprecedented arrival of New World bird species (*Brit. Birds*, 62:493) tends to support the claim that *plexippus* can, and does, cross the Atlantic unaided. Mention should also be made of an almost certain record of one in a lucerne field at North Fambridge in 1948 (ADB).

*Pararge megera* L. (Wall Brown)
Generally distributed and common.

*Pararge aegeria* L. (Speckled Wood)
The only Essex species of butterfly which is currently increasing and extending its range. The VCH stated that it had been common in the nineteenth century but had practically vanished by 1900, although it had still been common in Epping Forest *c.* 1890. It was noted during the first half of this century only at Westcliff-on-Sea (3) in 1933 (*Essex Nat.*, 29:207), Lexden, Colchester, in 1938 (JF), High Laver in 1939 and Hainault Forest in 1943 (*Essex Nat.*, 29:208) and at Bullock Wood, Colchester, in the 1940s (DC). Single specimens were seen at Bell Common, Epping Forest, on 11 October 1953 (*Essex Nat.*, 29:208); at Chingford in 1956, possibly a progeny of a few released in the area in 1953 (*Essex Nat.*, 32:159); and in Hatfield Forest on 16 July 1955 (GHBS), but one on Hadleigh Downs on 9 May 1954 (LSE) can perhaps be claimed to have provided the first sign of what was to become a re-colon-

isation of Essex, presumably from Kent where it had been spreading eastwards, the first small colony having been discovered by DGD at Langdon Hills in 1955. By the early 1960s it had become widespread and locally common in a wide belt along the north bank of the Thames estuary from Rochford west to Grays (HCH, RT) and it is continuing to consolidate in this area.

Meanwhile the species has spread north and is now (1974) established in the Brentwood area (KWG, GS *et al.*); at South Hanningfield (SH, JTS); Danbury Ridge (FBM, LTS *et al.*); Maldon (PJ) and at Bradwell-on-Sea (AJD). To the west it appeared at Woodford Green in 1972 and 1973 (*Countryside*, 22:218). Beyond this range stragglers have been seen at Navestock/Coxtie Green (PJW); Chelmsford in 1965 (GAP); Tiptree in 1967 (JF); Fingringhoe Wick N.R. (the northernmost locality to date) in 1971 (ENT) and Little Leighs in 1972 (WKS).

*Eumenis semele* L. (Grayling)

Very local: virtually confined to the north-east where it appears to be declining. Until the mid-1960s it was common south of Colchester at Berechurch, Layer-de-la-Haye and East Donyland, extending into Colchester where it frequently occurred in town gardens (JF). Other north-east Essex localities in which it has been found are Birch, Copford, Coggeshall and Langenhoe (JF), Mistley (CPR) and, in 1949, Weeley (*Essex Nat.*, 28:211). Two found *in cop.* on Skipper's Island N.R., Hamford Water, on 7 August 1956 (EFW), is the only record for that locality.

It is still found on the War Department lands on the southern outskirts of Colchester (e.g., 12 at Berechurch in August 1971) but has much declined (JF). Another colony still exists at West Bergholt (JF) but at Fingringhoe Wick N.R. and Colne Point N.R. on either side of the Colne Estuary, where strong colonies were present up to the late 1960s, *semele* suddenly became rare although a partial recovery was evident at the latter locality in 1974 (ENT).

Several were seen near Bradwell-on-Sea between 1948 and 1953 (AJD)—perhaps a short-lived extension of range across the Colne/Blackwater Estuaries. Individuals at North Fambridge on 5 August 1950 (*Essex Nat.*, 28:294), 29 July 1951 (*Essex Nat.*, 29:45) and 19 July 1959 (JTF) may have reflected a still further temporary extension of range of the north-east Essex population, but occasional examples on the Hadleigh/Benfleet Downs over the years (HCH) were possibly stragglers from Kent. Other individuals were seen at Birchanger in 1939 (GTN), at Maldon on 17 August 1947 (GAP) and near Fryerning *c.* 1947 (*Essex Nat.*, 28:210).

*Maniola jurtina* L. (Meadow Brown)

Generally distributed and common, though less plentiful than formerly. A large and particular brightly marked form flourished at Weeley until the 1950s (ADB).

*Maniola tithonus* L. (Gatekeeper)
Generally distributed and often very common in suitable localities.

*Coenonympha pamphilus* L. (Small Heath)
Still common in grassy places but has decreased to a marked extent in some localities as a result of the waste land and heaths it inhabits becoming overgrown with rank vegetation and scrub after myxamatosis decimated local rabbit populations.

*Aphantopus hyperantus* L. (Ringlet)
Still to be found over much of the county in suitable localities, but in some areas it is now at low density as a result of scrub encroachment and has disappeared from others due to the same cause. By no means confined to large areas of woodland, it is also found here and there in sparsely timbered districts—an example being the colony on remote Skipper's Island N.R., Hamford Water (CEC). Aberration *caeca* Fuchs, which has only a few 'blind' spots on the underside, has occurred on several occasions in Friday Wood, Berechurch (JF *et al.*), and ab. *obsoleta* Tutt was found in the same locality in August 1956 (W. Simpson *per* JF).

*Melanargia galathea* L. (Marbled White)
Confined to south-east Essex: now extremely local and scarce. The VCH, after citing one or two records from the north of the county, stated that it occurred freely in south Essex, and this was still the case up to *c*. 1956 (HCH). Indeed, in 1950 it was described as occurring in greater numbers to the west of Southend-on-Sea (*Essex Nat.*, 28:291) and on the north bank of the Crouch Estuary (*Essex Nat.*, 28:294) than in any previous year, and an example was seen as far north as Woodham Mortimer between Maldon and Danbury (*Essex Nat.*, 28:297). The next year it colonised an area on the north bank of the River Crouch between Battlesbridge and Wickford (*Essex Nat.*, 29:42) and was said 'still' to occur locally in the Brentwood area (*London Nat.*, 29:56). It is also stated to have been adundant near Ingatestone up to *c*. 1960 but absent subsequently (W. G. Campbell *per* EFW). In the late 1950s a steady decline and contraction of range set in, with the result that for some years it has been confined, in desperately small numbers, to a few restricted localities in the Rochford Hundred (DGD, RAS *et al.*) where it should on no account be collected.

*Apatura iris* L. (Purple Emperor)
Very rare; probably extinct. Of this aristocrat among our native butterflies the VCH stated that it had become exceedingly rare, while adding that it seemed to have occurred in all the larger Essex woods in the past and 'doubtless still existed in some of them'. Among old records in the literature, outstanding is one of 80–100 seen in woodland at St. Osyth in 1842 (*Entomologist*, 1:

384). Since the turn of the century there have been several rumoured reports of its occurrence in various localities, but the only record regarded as fully authentic concerns a single insect which was well seen in a wood at Weeley in north-east Essex *c.* 1956 (ADB). What was almost certainly another was watched in East Wood, Colchester (a traditional locality), *c.* 1953 (AI).

*Limenitis camilla* L. (White Admiral)

Formerly widespread: now very local and scarce and apparently confined to south Essex. The VCH stated that this graceful species was virtually confined to north Essex, and this remained the position until the early 1930s when it began to extend its range southwards and westwards, eventually reaching most points of the county. It was noted in Epping Forest in 1932 (*Proc. S. Lond. ent. nat. Hist Soc.*, 1932-3:94) and was common on Danbury Ridge in 1935 (GAP). First seen in the Southend/Benfleet area in 1936 (*Entomologist*, 71:33; *Proc. S. Lond. ent. nat. Hist. Soc.*, 1936-7: 27), it subsequently became widespread throughout south-east Essex as well as in the woods between Maldon and North Fambridge (JTF). In 1937 it was seen in Hatfield Forest (PBMA), where it was common by 1946 (BSCHNS); in 1942 at Saffron Walden (*Entomologist*, 75:203); in 1945 in Ongar Park Woods (*Essex Nat.*, 27:306) and Parndon (*Essex Nat.* 27:37); in 1947 at Emerson Park, Hornchurch (BPH); and in 1949 at Ugley (CC). Small numbers were found at High Woods, Blackmore, in 1951–52 but not subsequently (RRC) and it was described as plentiful at Brentwood in 1952 (*Essex Nat.*, 29:110).

The subsequent decline of *L. camilla* is poorly documented. It was present in Hatfield Forest up to at least 1955 (GHBS) and died out on Danbury Ridge (GAP) and between Maldon and North Fambridge (*Essex Nat.*, 31:157) prior to 1960. It was last seen at Emerson Park in 1960 (BPH) and in the Colchester area in 1964 (JF). The only subsequent records are: Hazeleigh Wood, one in 1965 (GAP, TAP); Stondon Massey near Ongar, noted on several occasions up to 1967 (J. Winkworth *per* DCT); Passingford Bridge, two in 1967 (*Essex Nat.*, 32:159); Langdon Hills, relict colony (RT); Benfleet, Rochford and Hockley areas, a few still survive (HCH).

In 1947 examples of a second brood were found during September at Westcliff-on-Sea, Ongar Park Woods and Colchester (*Entomologist*, 81:170). An example of ab. *obliterae* Robson & Gardner was taken at Takeley (= 'Ukeley') on 8 July 1950 (*Proc. S. Lond. ent. nat. Hist. Soc.*, 1951–2:40) and another was captured in Donyland Woods on 2 August 1955 (JP: *Colchester nat. Hist. Soc Ann. Rep.*, 1962, with photograph).

*Vanessa atalanta* L. (Red Admiral)

Annual immigrant: widely distributed and fairly common in some years but decidedly scarce in others. The years of exceptional

29

abundance mentioned in the VCH appear to be a thing of the past.

*Vanessa cardui* L. (Painted Lady)

Immigrant: still occurs annually but fluctuates widely in numbers. In some years extremely scarce, with a mere handful of individuals on and near the coast, but in others, e.g. 1969, fairly common and widespread.

*Nymphalis io* L. (Peacock)

Generally distributed and common but less abundant than formerly; spraying of nettles, notably on roadside verges, is probably a major factor in its decline.

*Nymphalis antiopa* L. (Camberwell Beauty)

Rare immigrant. This fine butterfly, so aptly called the Mourning Cloak in the New World, has been reported during the past 50 years from: Leigh-on-Sea, 1931 (RAS); near North Weald, 7 August 1932 (*Entomologist*, 65: 258); Chingford (*Essex Nat.*, 27: 305) and Bradwell-on-Sea (W. G. Thurgood, *per* AJD; *Entomologist*, 79:106), 1945; Emerson Park, Hornchurch, 1947 (BPH); near Southend-on-Sea, 1948 (*Entomologist*, 81:123); Ongar Park Woods, 10 April 1948 (*Entomologist* 81:163); Old Heath, Colchester, September 1958 (F. V. Duckworth *per* JF); Ingatestone, 22 September 1971 (R. B. Collard *per* EFW).

*Nymphalis polychloros* L. (Large Tortoiseshell)

Periodic: virtually absent from the county at the present time. This fine butterfly seems to have been widely distributed and often fairly common up to *c.* 1910, but subsequently to have been mainly confined to the larger woods in north and north-east Essex from the Colchester area and Marks Hall Woods, Coggeshall, north to the Stour Valley, although it was taken at Newport in the west in 1920 (Douglas Watson coll.) and may well have survived undetected in other little-visited localities. One taken at Bocking *c.* 1936 (*Entomologist*, 69:215) may have been the first sign of a major extension of range which became evident by 1942 when specimens were seen in south-east Essex (HCH). It appeared in Hatfield Forest (BSCNHS) in 1945 and at Ugley (PBMA, CC) in 1946, a year after a number that had been obtained in north-east Essex were released just over the Hertfordshire boundary at Bishop's Stortford (*Trans. Bishop's Stortford nat. Hist. Soc.*, 1; *List of Lepidoptera*: 6), thus casting doubt on the origin of specimens subsequently recorded in west Essex.

By 1946 *polychloros* was widely distributed around Maldon (GAP *et al.*) and in 1948 was noted at Frinton-on-Sea and in Epping Forest (*Entomologist*, 81:150) and at Takeley (CC). The decline in its recently-won territories, which finally led to its virtual disappearance, appears to have been as sudden as its arrival. None was seen in south-east Essex (HCH) or in the Maldon district (GAP) after 1950, and single specimens at Chelmsford on 11 July 1952

(GAP) and in Hatfield Forest on 5 May 1956 (CC) are the only subsequent records away from north Essex. There it was last seen (at Berechurch, West Bergholt and Marks Hall, Coggeshall) in spring 1954 (JF).

Only two later records are admissible, viz., one on The Naze at Walton on 21 September 1969 (JKW *et al.*) and another on *Buddleia* at Westcliff-on-Sea on 7 August 1973 (HCH). The possibility that the former was an example of the very similar but rather larger *Nymphalis xanthomelas* Esp. (the Eastern Tortoiseshell) which was taken in Kent in 1953 (*Ent. Gaz.*, 14:108–9) cannot, however, be excluded.

*Aglais urticae* L. (Small Tortoiseshell)

Universally distributed and common. Although in some years it still approaches abundance locally, it is generally less numerous than formerly. An example of the almost white aberration *semialba* Frohawk was taken in a lucerne field at Copford, near Colchester, on 4 August 1953 (JF).

*Polygonia c-album* L. (Comma)

Widely distributed and often fairly common. Although apparently common in south-west Essex in the early 1800s (*Essex Nat.*, 5:88–89) this fine species was otherwise known only as an occasional straggler to Essex before the 1930s when it rapidly colonised the county. It first appeared, at Walthamstow (*Entomologist*, 67:9) and in the Southend-on-Sea area (*Entomologist*, 71:33), in 1933 and was common at Maldon by 1935 (GAP) when it was also recorded at Romford and Loughton (*Entomologist*, 69:139) and in the Bishop's Stortford area (*Trans. Bishop's Stortford nat. Hist. Soc.,* 1; *List of Lepidoptera*: 6), and at about that time at Colchester (ADB). By 1937 it was fairly numerous in south-east Essex (*Entomologist*, 71:33) and on Danbury Ridge (GAP) and had reached Dovercourt (*Entomologist*, 71:12); and in 1939 it was noted in Hatfield Forest (BSCNHS). By the mid-1940s, when it was reported from a number of additional localities, its distribution was almost county-wide. This is a position *c-album* has maintained, though numbers fluctuate markedly and in some years it is decidedly scarce in certain areas.

An example of ab. *sagitta* Frohawk, which has the hindwings suffused with dark brown, was captured in Friday Wood, Berechurch, on 21 July 1958 (JF).

*Argynnis paphia* L. (Silver-washed Fritillary)

Apparently absent from the county at the present time. The VCH stated that this fine butterfly was locally common in north-east Essex but that it had practically disappeared from Epping Forest where it had formerly abounded. The only record from the southern half of the county during the first three decades of the present century was of a worn female at Woodford in August 1926 (*Entomologist*, 59:276) but in the 1930s it began to appear in small numbers in other areas—at Manuden in 1934–35 (PBMA), on Danbury Ridge in 1936 (GAP) and in Hazeleigh Wood in 1937 (GAP). In 1941 it was found in Hatfield Forest (PBMA) and in south-east Essex (*Essex Nat.*, 29:108), and in 1945 at Loughton (*Entomologist*, 79:118) and Parndon (*Essex Nat.* 28:36).

By 1947 *paphia* was common in Hazeleigh Wood (GAP) and 'quite abundant' in Hatfield Forest (*Essex Nat.*, 28:79), and by 1948 was well represented in the woods between Maldon and North Fambridge (*Essex Nat.*, 31:157). In 1949 seven were seen in two woods near Saffron Walden (*Entomologist*, 84:112) and it was noted at Ugley (CC). In 1950 four were seen near Ingatestone (*Entomologist*, 183:237); in 1951–52 small numbers were present at High Woods, Blackmore (RRC); and in 1952 it was stated to have reappeared 'recently' in the Brentwood district (*Essex Nat.*, 29:110).

Meanwhile, by 1950 the butterfly had deserted south-east Essex, where its density had remained low (HCH), but it was apparently the late 1950s before a general and rapid decline set in.

In north-east Essex it was often common in woodland south and east of Colchester in the 1940s and up to 1958 when it suddenly vanished from its strongholds in the Colchester area at Berechurch, Donyland, West Bergholt, Stanway and Tiptree (JF; *Colchester nat. Hist. Soc., Ann. Rep.*, 1962). It was last reported from Hatfield Forest in 1955 (GHBS) and although it had still been well represented in the woods between Maldon and North Fambridge in 1957 (*Essex Nat.*, 30:123) it had completely died out in this district by 1960 (*Essex Nat.*, 31:157) as well as on Danbury Ridge (GAP). The only subsequent record is of one in Matching Park near Harlow in 1962 (RJD) and it would appear, therefore, to have deserted the county—one can but hope only temporarily.

The greenish ab. *valezina* Esp., the principal stronghold of which is in the New Forest, Hants, was noted on a number of occasions in the woods south of Colchester between the mid-1940s and early 1950s (ADB, JF, CGM) and one was also seen on Danbury Ridge in the mid-1930s (A. C. Edwards *per* GAP).

*Argynnis cydippe* L. (High Brown Fritillary)

Apparently absent from the county at the present time. Formerly the most widespread of the larger fritillaries, this species was widely distributed and sometimes common in well-wooded districts in the north, centre and south-west of the county until the mid-1950s when, as in the case of the last species, a decline set in. This resulted in its virtual disappearance from Essex.

It is clear that it extended its range in the late 1930s and early 1940s as it appeared in the south-east Essex woodlands (*Essex. Nat.*, 29:42) and in Hatfield Forest (BSCNHS) just before the 1939–45 war, and at Parndon (*Essex Nat.*, 28:36) and Farnham gravel-pits near Bishop's Stortford (DAA) in 1945; also several were seen in Hazeleigh Wood near Maldon in 1947 (GAP). Although a decline was apparent in south-east Essex as early as 1948 (DGD) it was still 'abundant' in the Brentwood district (*Essex Nat.*, 29:110) and common in the Fryerning/Blackmore area (RRC) in 1952. During the early 1950s it was still fairly common in the woods around Colchester, though a marked decline had set in by 1956 at Donyland, Berechurch and High Woods (ADB, JF) and it was last seen in the area in Donyland Woods in 1958 (JF). It was last observed in south-east Essex at Hadleigh in 1960 (HCH) but its disappearance from remaining areas went unrecorded. Apart from a fritillary, almost certainly of this species, on Danbury Ridge in July 1963 (GAP), the only subsequent record is of one in Thorndon Park on 3 July 1966 (RRC).

*Argynnis aglaia* L. (Dark Green Fritillary)
Formerly very local; now rare. The VCH cited only old records from north-east Essex, but it existed at Hadleigh until 1934 when its locality was destroyed by building (HCH; *Essex Nat.*, 29:328). It was found in small to moderate numbers on Danbury Ridge from 1936–38 (GAP; *Entomologist*, 71:213), at Loughton in 1943 (*Entomologist*, 79:118), at Farnham gravel-pits near Bishop's Stortford in 1945 (DAA) and in Hatfield Forest for several years up to 1947 (PBMA, BSCNHS, GHBS).

All subsequent records have come from south Essex and all but one of them from the Brentwood area: there it was described as sparse in one locality in 1949 (*London Nat.*, 29:59), common in South Weald Park from 1950–52 (RRC) and not uncommon in certain areas in the latter year (*Essex Nat.*, 29:110). More recently, single specimens were seen at Ingrave on 4 August 1965 (*Ent. Rec.*, 77:240), in Thorndon Park on 20 August 1970 (PF) and at Chigwell Row on 29 August 1971 (IS). In the light of the foregoing, two examples either of *cydippe* or *aglaia* seen in Epping Forest on 25 July 1974 (VV) are more likely to have been the latter.

Thus the foothold of *aglaia* as well as that of the two preceding species (if they still exist anywhere in the county) is very slender indeed and we can but hope that the large fritillaries may one day return to grace some of their old haunts. An explanation for their disappearance and that of *L. camilla* (above) is not easy to find. Possibly a number of factors played their part, lack of woodland management, forestry changes, scrub encroachment and a series of wet summers in the 1950s among them.

*Clossiana euphrosyne* L. (Pearl-bordered Fritillary)
Formerly our commonest fritillary, having been found in the past in well-wooded districts throughout the county, it has not been recorded for several years. Its decline began later than that of the larger fritillaries as it continued to occupy a number of sites throughout the 1950s and survived well into the 1960s. The years

c 33

in which it deserted various parts of the county are incompletely recorded. But it was last seen in South Weald Park *c.* 1956 (JTS), in the Colchester area at Berechurch in 1961 (JF), and on Danbury Ridge (GAP) and in the south-east Essex woodlands (HCH) as recently as 1968. Save that there is some evidence of its continued existence in a locality in the extreme north-east of the county, there is no indication that it still occurs anywhere in Essex. *If found it should not be collected, a remark which applies equally to any of the larger fritillaries previously mentione*d.

*Clossiana selene* Schiff. (Small Pearl-bordered Fritillary)
Probably extinct. The VCH claimed that it was fairly common and sometimes abundant and inferred that it was generally distributed in suitable localities. If this was so it must certainly have declined dramatically during the first two or three decades of the present century as, apart from the fact that it was introduced in 1937 and again in 1940 into Belfairs N.R., Hadleigh, where it survived until *c.* 1948 (HCH), it has been reported during the past fifty years only from Little Leighs, where small numbers were present up to the mid-1930s (WKS), and the Brentwood area, where it was said to be still common in 1949 (*London Nat.,* 29:59) and again in 1952 (*Essex Nat.,* 29:110). There is no evidence that it occurs anywhere in Essex today.

*Melitaea athalia* Rott. (Heath Fritillary)
Extinct as an indigenous species; introduced stock dying out. This species was to be found in several woods in north-east Essex in the last century but became extinct in its last stronghold—in the Dedham area—*c.* 1890 (VCH). Specimens from these localities were said to have been larger and more richly-coloured than any occurring elsewhere in England.

Its inclusion in this post-1925 list, therefore, results from introductions which have since been made. *M. athalia* was introduced into Hadleigh Woods in south-east Essex in 1925 and into Hockley Woods in 1935 (HCH), and for some years it was common intermittently in both localities. However, for several years it has been very scarce in its restricted haunts and now seems on the verge of extinction as an Essex species, none having been seen in 1972 (DGD). Examples of the black ab. *cymothoe* Bertolini were taken at Hadleigh in June 1940 (JAC, HCH).

*Thecla quercus* L. (Purple Hairstreak)
Widely distributed in wooded areas where the oak is well represented, and even in some districts with little woodland such as in the vicinity of the coast at Bradwell-on-Sea (AJD). Numbers have fluctuated widely from year to year but whereas up to the 1940s it sometimes approached abundance locally, it has not been reported as really common anywhere since 1948 when it was abundant in Belfairs N.R., Hadleigh (HCH). It has maintained reasonable num-

bers in the woods around Colchester, particularly Friday Wood, Berechurch, where larvae were widespread in May 1970 (JF). The butterflies were much more in evidence throughout the county in the fine summers of 1970 and 1971.

*Strymonidia w-album* Knoch (White-letter Hairstreak)
Local, with colonies scattered throughout the county where there are stands of elm and wych elm. There has inevitably been some loss of ground in a county as intensively farmed and developed as Essex, and the high incidence of Dutch Elm disease since 1971 has led to many traditional sites being destroyed. Nevertheless strong colonies are known still to exist in the Colchester area, notably at Friday Wood (Berechurch), Donyland Woods and West Bergholt (JF), and in parts of east, central and south-east Essex.

*Callophrys rubi* L. (Green Hairstreak)
Also local, its presence in a particular area depending on whether broom and/or gorse, its food-plants, grow freely there. Often quite common where it occurs, it does not seem to have decreased to any marked degree where its habitat has remained intact. It is particularly well-represented on Danbury Ridge (GAP) and on the Ministry of Defence heathlands south of Colchester (JF). However, it appears to have been little met with in the west of the county: Hatfield Forest (BSCNHS) and Manuden (CM) are the only localities mentioned in the literature but it was recorded at Matching in the late 1950s (RJD).

*Lycaena phlaeas* L. (Small Copper)
Widely distributed and still common where areas of rough ground or heathland continue to provide optimum conditions for it. However, as with other small butterflies which inhabit open ground and whose larvae feed on low-growing plants, more and more traditional sites are being lost through building operations, agricultural cultivations, scrub encroachment or crop spraying.

*Lampides boeticus* L. (Long-tailed Blue)
A very rare immigrant, this almost cosmopolitan species has been recorded only twice for certain. A female, probably accompanied by males of the same species, was taken while fluttering around a large plant of *Lathyrus latifolius* (Everlasting Pea)—one of its food plants—at Dedham in the summer of 1931 (*Entomologist*, 64:179). The second record was also of a female, settled on an antirrhinum flower at Walton-on-the-Naze on 1 October 1932 (*Entomologist*, 65:259). What was almost certainly another example of this migratory blue settled on a flower of *Hieraceum* sp. at Fingringhoe Wick N.R. in September 1970 (SEL) but flew off before its identity could be fully established.

*Plebejus argus* L. (Silver-studded Blue)
Rare; possibly extinct. The VCH gave the Epping district as the only area in which this little blue was to be found, but there are

no recent records from that locality, although in 1949 a flourishing colony was reported from the Brentwood area (*London Nat.*, 26: 69) and one was taken at Fryerning (*Essex Nat.*, 28:210). More recently, in 1953, a small colony of the chalk form *cretacea* Tutt, which occurs in north Kent, was found in an old chalk quarry at Grays (HCH *et al.*) but this became extinct, probably as a result of encroachment of scrub and rank vegetation, *c.* 1960. It is believed that this is the only colony of *cretacea* to have been recorded north of the Thames. It is not known to occur in the county at the present time.

*Aricia agestis* Schiff. (Brown Argus)

Very local. The VCH described this blue as one of our commonest butterflies but this is certainly not true today. It has disappeared from many of its former haunts due to one or other of the causes mentioned under *L. phlaeas* (above). It possibly survives undetected in under-recorded areas and may occasionally be overlooked where it flies with *P. icarus* (below) but there is no doubt that it has become extremely local. A few small pockets remain in the north-east (ADB, JF) and in the south-east (DGD, HCH) while there is still a colony in the Dengie Peninsula (AJD) and another was found at East Tilbury in 1971 (RT), but most recent reports concern the demise of colonies such as those at Mucking, where the site was destroyed subsequently to 1966 (RT), and Danbury Ridge, where grubbing up of rough ground put paid to it *c.* 1967 (CH).

*Polyommatus icarus* Rott. (Common Blue)

Widely distributed in varying numbers and often locally common, particularly on the coast and estuaries along stretches of sea-wall and adjacent waste ground.

*Lysandra coridon* Poda (Chalk-hill Blue)

Apart from the fact that, surprisingly, it became locally common in Epping Forest for some years from 1859 (*Essex Nat.*, 5:104) and at Colchester (High Woods) some time prior to 1870 (*Butterflies and Moths of the British Isles*), this fine blue is but a rare wanderer to Essex from chalk districts to the south or west. Stragglers have been reported during the past half-century from Childerditch Common on 19 August 1932 (*Entomologist*, 65:260), Hadleigh Downs in August 1934 and August 1935 (2) (HCH), Great Warley on 25 August 1946 (EFW) and Havering in 1950 (RRC).

*Celastrina argiolus* L. (Holly Blue)

Widespread; erratic. The statement in the VCH that this blue is widely distributed but often scarce in some districts holds good today. After several lean years it was widespread and locally numerous from 1967–71 but it has not been much in evidence since. Removal of many old ivy-covered trees may well have adversely affected the distribution of the species in some districts as it depends on ivy for its second brood.

*Pyrgus malvae* L. (Grizzled Skipper)

Local; declining. This species has undoubtedly decreased drastically since the VCH described it as widely distributed and common in many places. The localities that it still inhabits, which are scattered throughout the county, more particularly in the eastern half, are still too numerous to list, but it has disappeared from a number of its former haunts and is threatened in others due to scrub encroachment or building operations.

*Erynnis tages* L. (Dingy Skipper)

Decidedly local; declining. The VCH gave its only known localities as Epping Forest, the Colchester district and Harwich, but it must have been much more widespread than that as even today, although it has suffered from the same disturbances as *P. malvae*, small colonies are known to exist in the Benfleet area (DGD, HCH), on Danbury Ridge (GAP), in Grays Chalk Quarry N.R. (GAP) and, in the north-east, at Berechurch, West Bergholt, Fingringhoe, Marks Tey and Stanway (JF) and at Fingringhoe Wick N.R. (GAP). Other places in which it has been noted during the past three decades are Woodham Mortimer (*Essex Nat.,* 28:78), North Fambridge (*Essex Nat.*, 29:44), Chigwell (KWG), Havering (Bedfords Park) and South Weald Park (RRC), Great Warley (EFW) and Hatfield Forest (BSCNHS).

*Thymelicus sylvestris* Poda (Small Skipper)

Widespread and common in suitable localities, i.e. waste ground, heaths and woodland clearings.

*Thymelicus lineola* Ochs. (Essex Skipper)

Fairly widespread. This skipper is so similar to *T. sylvestris*, with which it frequently flies, that it was not discovered as a British species until 1890 from specimens taken at Dovercourt, hence its vernacular name. It is common in many of the still undeveloped parts of the coast and estuary lands, particularly along sea walls and in grassy waste places. It occurs locally well inland such as in the Brentwood district where it is widespread (*London Nat.*, 29:80; *Proc. Brit. ent. nat. Hist. Soc.*, 1(2):119), on Danbury Ridge (GAP), and in west Essex at Manuden and Ugley (PBMA) and in Hatfield Forest (BSCNHS).

*Ochlodes venata* Br. & Grey (Large Skipper)

Widespread and common in suitable localities.


## HETEROCERA (MOTHS)

*Mimas tiliae* L. (Lime Hawk)

Generally distributed, its density ranging from low to fairly high, depending on the prevalence of lime trees: thus it can be rather sparsely represented in well-wooded districts, e.g. Danbury Ridge

(GAP), yet fairly numerous in built-up areas, e.g. Collier Row, Romford (RRC).

*Laothoe populi* L. (Poplar Hawk)
Generally distributed; common in many districts, and where poplars are plentiful it can be the most abundant hawk moth.

*Smerinthus ocellata* L. (Eyed Hawk)
Generally distributed in small to moderate numbers and at times locally common.

*Acherontia atropos* L. (Death's Head Hawk)
The largest British species, this magnificent insect, with a skull-and-crossbones likeness on its thorax, is a well-known immigrant which is probably of annual occurrence, although it is usually scarce and sometimes rare. From time to time, however, it appears in large numbers, though this has not been the case since 1956 when six occurred at Bradwell-on-Sea alone (AJD). Generally it appears to have been much less in evidence since the advent of wholesale spraying of potato crops on which most females lay their eggs. As with other migrants it has most often been recorded on or near the coast, but the literature cites a number of inland occurrences which are too numerous to list, though there have been few since 1960.

*Herse convolvuli* L. (Convolvulus Hawk)
This large hawk moth, with a wingspan equal to that of *A. atropos*, is also an immigrant. Like the last species it is probably of annual occurrence, though usually scarce, but is periodically quite common, as in 1946 when many were seen at Great Wakering (DGD), and 1956 when a total of 13 was recorded at Bradwell-on-Sea (AJD). In common with a number of other immigrants it has been markedly less in evidence during the past decade, and this is reflected in the almost complete absence of records from the interior of the county.

*Sphinx ligustri* L. (Privet Hawk)
Widely distributed. Except in some well-wooded districts, where it is fairly common in some years, it appears to occur today generally at fairly low density. The native stock is probably reinforced periodically by immigrants.

*Hyloicus pinastri* L. (Pine Hawk)
Very rare vagrant. The VCH omitted the occurrence of one near Harwich in June 1872 (*Entomologist*, 7:46) and the only subsequent records are of one at Lexden, Colchester, on 7 August 1956 (JF) and another at Bradwell-on-Sea on 25 June 1959 (AJD). Its virtual absence is surprising when one recalls that it has long been established in the coniferous forests of east Suffolk.

*Celerio galii* Rott. (Bedstraw Hawk)
Irregular immigrant, recorded in six years between 1952 and 1973 inclusive at Bradwell-on-Sea where, exceptionally, 14 occurred in

1955 but otherwise singles except for two in 1972 and three in 1973
(AJD). The only other records during the past half century come
from inland localities, i.e. near Chelmsford at end August 1938
(*Entomologist*, 72:14) and at Stanway, Colchester (full-grown
larva), in mid-September 1973 (T. C. Hitchman *per* JF).

*Celerio livornica* Esp. (Striped Hawk)
  Rare immigrant. Records since 1925, all of single specimens and
involving a surprising number of inland localities, come from
Leigh-on-Sea in 1928 (*per* HCH); Becontree on 20 May 1931 and
Springfield (='Springbank'), Chelmsford, on 11 June 1931 (*Entomologist*, 64: 163–4); Great Baddow on 4 July 1944 (*Entomologist*,
78:55); Newport (24 July), Shenfield and Chelmsford, in 1946
(*Entomologist*, 80:139); North Fambridge on 7 June 1949 (*Entomologist*, 82:204); and Bradwell-on-Sea on 20 and 31 August and
1 September 1949 and 25 June 1950 (AJD).

*Hippotion celerio* L. (Silver-striped Hawk)
  This hawk moth was at one time a not infrequent visitor (see
VCH), but it has only appeared twice during the past half century
—at Bradwell-on-Sea on 6 October 1961 (AJD) and Thames Haven
in the same year (RS).

*Daphnis nerii* L. (Oleander Hawk)
  There are three Essex records of this exotic southern hawk moth,
viz. two (one inside the Cock Inn) at Boreham *c.* 1933 (W. P.
Seabrook coll.) and one at Leigh-on-Sea on 1 October 1948
(VGR; HCH coll.).

*Deilephila porcellus* L. (Small Elephant Hawk)
  Decidedly local and usually scarce where it does occur. The VCH
stated that it was widely distributed, mainly on the coast. However, its status today appears to be very different as it has occurred
sparsely along the littoral only at Maldon in 1936 (GAP), Creeksea
in 1935–36 (HCH), Canewdon in 1936 (HCH), Bradwell from 1950–
55 (AJD), Hockley in 1956 (DM), Westcliff-on-Sea in 1958 (HCH)
and Dovercourt in 1964 (MEA), whereas in recent years it has been
recorded most consistently in the area centred on Brentwood where
it occurs in small numbers annually at Ingrave (KWG) and has been
found during the past few years at Thorndon and South Weald
Parks (RRC), Hutton (EFW), Margaretting (RU) and, further north,
near Ongar (DCT). It is stated to be rare on Danbury Ridge (CH,
FBM), and Thames-side (RT), and to have been present in 1945 in
Hatfield Forest (BSCNHS). It is unknown inland in north-east
Essex (JF) and the only recent record from the south-west concerns
two in the Chigwell/Lambourne area in 1972 (IS).

*Deilephila elpenor* L. (Elephant Hawk)
  Widely distributed and common (probably increased) in many
districts, sharing with *L. populi* the distinction of being the most
common hawk moth taking the county as a whole.

*Macroglossum stellatarum* L. (Humming-bird Hawk)
Immigrant: still recorded annually, though it has been scarce, and frequently rare, for a number of years. In common with other immigrants its numbers have always fluctuated widely from year to year. Formerly it was described in some years as 'swarming' or 'very numerous', even in localities well inland, but it has not appeared in strength since 1959 when (as also in four years between 1947 and 1952) it was well represented and widespread. During the past decade the trend seems to have been towards even greater scarcity, and inland records have been few and far between.

*Hemaris fuciformis* L. (Broad-bordered Bee Hawk)
Formerly found in 'all woods where bugle and campion flowers abound' (VCH): now very rare and perhaps extinct. The only comparatively recent records are: Hadleigh Woods, scarce up to 1947 (HCH); Weeley, a few in 1949 (*Essex Nat.*, 28:211); Ongar Park Woods, recorded 'recently', i.e. prior to 1953 (*London Nat.*, 33: 114); Colchester (High Woods), two on 20 May 1957 (JF).

*Harpyia bifida* Brahm (Poplar Kitten)
Widely distributed but nowhere common, occurring at low density over much of the county.

*Harpyia furcula* Clerck (Sallow Kitten)
Widely distributed and markedly less scarce than the last species, though nowhere really common.

*Cerura vinula* L. (Puss Moth)
Generally distributed; has declined. This sizeable and attractive moth, with its striking larva, was stated in the VCH to be common everywhere. It must, therefore, have decreased considerably as, although it is still generally distributed, it cannot be described as really numerous anywhere today and its density is low in a number of areas.

*Stauropus fagi* L. (Lobster)
Local. The Essex stronghold of this species, which was described by the VCH as scarce but widely distributed and which takes its name from the remarkable larva, is Epping Forest from which it has been reported frequently (*London Nat.*, 33:116) and in which as many as 20 males came to light in June 1937 (*Entomologist*, 71: 26). It is, however, quite common on Danbury Ridge (GAP) and widespread though mostly at low density in the Brentwood area, having been noted at Ingrave (KWG), Thorndon Park (PCF), Hookend (RRC), Doddinghurst (JTS) and Coxtie Green (PJW). Elsewhere it has been reported from the Ongar area (DCT) and as very scarce at Benfleet and Hadleigh (HCH), while single examples were recorded at Lexden, Colchester, in each of the years 1956–58 (JF) and at Great Bromley in 1973 (FDB). Two are recorded from Bradwell-on-Sea, in 1949 and 1953 (AJD). Most specimens have been of the dark phase.

*Drymonia dodonaea* Schiff. (Light Marbled Brown)
The VCH described this species as widely distributed at low density, yet today it seems to be very local. Its stronghold appears to be the woodlands between Brentwood and Chelmsford: there it was noted at Writtle *c*. 1967 (Writtle Ag. Coll. coll.), Fryerning on 23 May 1970 and 27 May 1973 (4) (RRC, RT), and at Margaretting on 17 June 1973 (GAP, RU). Otherwise it has been reported during the past half-century from Benfleet in May 1935 and Westcliff-on-Sea in May 1957 (HCH); Epping Forest in June 1937 (*Entomologist*, 71: 27); Hatfield Forest *c*. 1949 (PBMA); Bradwell-on-Sea annually from 1950–54 (AJD); Lexden (Colchester) and Donyland Woods, May–June 1956–57 (JF); Hamford Water in 1970 and 1972 (JBF); Aldham in 1971 (MRSM) and Birch Park in June 1974 (JF: CNHS).
*Chaonia ruficornis* Hufn. (Lunar Marbled Brown)
Widespread. This species has a far wider distribution than the last and is also much less scarce, although the VCH considered its status was similar to that of *dodonaea*. It perhaps occurs in most well-wooded districts containing oak but records suggest that it reaches its highest density in the woodland belts stretching northeast from Epping Forest to Danbury Ridge, and in the southeast.
*Pheosia tremula* Clerck (Greater Swallow Prominent)
Generally distributed and common in many districts, especially where poplars grow plentifully.
*Pheosia gnoma* F. (Lesser Swallow Prominent)
Fairly widespread but more local than the last species which it so closely resembles, and generally less common though quite numerous in some districts: indeed, its numbers far exceed those of *tremula* on Danbury Ridge (GAP).
*Notodonta ziczac* L. (Pebble Prominent)
Generally distributed and common in many districts.
*Notodonta dromedarius* L. (Iron Prominent)
Widespread and locally common, probably occurring in all districts where birch and/or alder flourish.
*Notodonta trepida* Esp. (Great Prominent)
Very local and scarce. The VCH indicated that it was widespread at low density and this is borne out by the literature, but today it seems to be established only in the woodland belt between Brentwood and Chelmsford: in that area several were noted on 29 April 1964 (RRC) and in May 1973 (WLC) at Blackmore; two in May 1970 and six in May 1973 at Fryerning (RRC, RT); and one at Margaretting in May 1971 (RT). It was also noted in Thorndon Park in 1973 (PCF). Otherwise it has been recorded in Hatfield Forest *c*. 1945 (PBMA, BSCNHS), Bradwell-on-Sea in May 1954 (AJD), Berechurch (2) in May 1960 (JF), and Ongar in June 1963 and May 1973 (DCT). There is no published record this century from Epping Forest but

41

it was formerly quite common in that area and may well still occur there.

*Lophopteryx cucullina* Schiff. (Maple Prominent)

Local and scarce. Chalk districts are the true home of this prominent, yet it is apparently established in a few Essex localities and has occurred casually in several others. In north-east Essex 4–5 came to light annually from 1956–61 at Lexden (Colchester), Great Horkesley and West Bergholt (JF) and one in 1973 at Great Bromley (FDB); one or two appear most years on Danbury Ridge (GAP); it is present in Grays Chalk Quarry N.R. (RT); and single specimens occurred at Ongar on 18 July 1963 (DCT), in Hatfield Forest on 26 June 1970 and near Takeley on 25 July 1972 (GHBS), and in Thorndon Park (WLC) and at Chelmsford (GAP) in July 1974. On or near the coast individuals have appeared at Bradwell-on-Sea on 13 July 1955 (AJD), Little Clacton on 6 July 1963 (*Essex Nat.*, 31:106), Walton-on-the-Naze on 5 July 1970 (JKW), Hamford Water in 1973 (JBF) and at Dovercourt annually (1–2) from 1967–71 (MEA).

*Lophopteryx capucina* L. (Coxcomb Prominent)

Generally distributed and common in most districts.

*Odontosia carmelita* Esp. (Scarce Prominent)

Apart from a pair in Ongar Park Wood in May 1843 (*Zoologist* 1:201), reported only from Epping Forest. In addition to the occasional 19th century records mentioned in the VCH it was taken there are recently as 1938 (*Proc. S. Lond. ent. nat. Hist. Soc.*, 1937–8:18).

*Pterostoma palpina* Clerck (Pale Prominent)

Generally distributed and common in many districts.

*Phalera bucephala* L. (Buff Tip)

This quite large and attractive species is also generally distributed and quite common over wide areas; its communal larvae are often abundant locally.

*Clostera curtula* L. (Large Chocolate Tip)

Widely distributed at low or fairly low density and probably to be found in most places where aspen grows. The localities from which it has been recorded in recent years are scattered throughout the county and are too numerous to list.

*Clostera pigra* Hufn. (Small Chocolate Tip)

Rare. According to the VCH this species 'abounded' on aspen and sallow at the turn of the century but the only records during the past half century are: larvae on aspen suckers in two Hadleigh woods annually until 1939 (HCH); singly to light at Westcliff-on-Sea in 1955 and 1956 (HCH).

*Habrosyne pyritoides* Hufn. (Buff Arches)

Generally distributed and common in many areas.

*Thyatira batis* L. (Peach Blossom)

A bramble feeder like the last species, this beautifully marked moth is more local than *H. pyritoides*, although still widespread. Fairly high density has been reported from Ongar Park Woods in 1929 (*Entomologist*, 63:42), Danbury Ridge (GAP), Langdon Hills (RT) and Chalkney Wood, Earls Colne, on the edge of cultivated black-berry plantations (FDB, JF), but it is noted as scarce throughout south-east Essex (DGD, HCH), on Thames-side (RT) and in west Essex (PBMA).

*Tethea ocularis* L. (Figure of Eighty)
Fairly widespread. This is one species which may have increased this century. The VCH reported it as scarce, whereas today it is fairly common in a number of well-timbered districts, though poorly represented in others. It is probably to be found wherever aspens and/or poplars grow freely. A high percentage is now melanic.

*Tethea or* Schiff. (Poplar Lutestring)
Decidedly local, in spite of the fact that the VCH described it as of general occurrence among aspens. Noted during the past 50 years only from: Ongar Park Woods, 1929 (*Entomologist*, 63:41); Birchanger, fairly common in 1929 (CSC) and abundant in 1935 (CM); Hatfield Forest, present in the 1940s (PBMA, BSCNHS); Benfleet/Hadleigh, not uncommon (HCH); Danbury Ridge, fairly common in one area (DGD, RT); Lexden (Colchester), present 1956–61 (JF); Bradwell-on-Sea, 29 May 1970 (AJD); Hamford Water, 20 July 1971 (JBF). It does not appear to have been noted either in Epping Forest or, with the exception of one at Dodding-hurst in 1971 (JTS), in the woods around Brentwood.

*Tethea duplaris* L. (Least Satin Lutestring)
This species, sometimes known as the Common Lutestring, seems to be fairly widespread. Reported as occurring in varying numbers, though nowhere plentifully, in several well-timbered localities, it is probably to be found in most districts where there is birch. A good proportion today is melanic.

*Tethea fluctuosa* Hübn. (Greater Satin Lutestring)
This is the rarest of the lutestrings and single specimens at Lexden, Colchester, in June 1956 and 1957 (JF) are the only Essex records.

*Asphalia diluta* Schiff. (Lesser Lutestring)
Very local. Of this species, which is sometimes called the Oak Lutestring, the VCH stated that it came 'freely to sugar' in the autumn. If this was intended to imply that it was widespread the opposite seems to be the case today. It is fairly common on Danbury Ridge (GAP) and scarce at Bradwell-on-Sea (AJD), Westcliff-on-Sea (HCH) and Thundersley (DGD), while the only other records this century concern larvae at Warley in 1933 (*Proc. S. Lond. ent. nat. Hist. Soc.*, 1933–4:15) and one at Dovercourt in September 1965 (MEA).

*Achlya flavicornis* L. (Yellow-horned Lutestring)
Fairly widespread. This early spring species is recorded from all extensively wooded localities, in the majority of which it is common, and will probably be found in most districts containing a good growth of birch.

*Polyploca ridens* F. (Frosted Green Lutestring)
Fairly widespread. Much the same remarks apply to this species as to the last, except that oak supplies the larval food. Dark forms now predominate.

*Orgyia recens* Hübn. (Scarce Vapourer)
Very rare; possibly extinct. Except for one taken in Epping Forest in June 1858 (*Ent. Weekly Intelligencer*, 2:115) and another 'near Maldon' (i.e., at Danbury) in August 1878 (*Entomologist* 6:223), this extremely local British species has only been reported in Essex from near Brentwood, where it was discovered in the early years of the present century. It is doubtful whether it still survives in this area as the last recorded occurrence (of larvae) dates back to 1935 (W. P. Seabrook coll.).

*Orgyia antiqua* L. (Common Vapourer)
Widespread; has declined. The VCH stated that it abounded everywhere and could sometimes be seen flying even in the streets of the larger towns. This is certainly not the case today: for a number of years it has been getting scarcer and although it is still fairly widespread and locally common, it is now far from numerous in some of its former strongholds and has disappeared from other areas where it had previously occurred at lower density.

*Dasychira pudibunda* L. (Pale Tussock)
Generally distributed; common in well-wooded districts.

*Euproctis chrysorrhoea* L. (Brown Tail)
Regarded as virtually a maritime species in the British Isles, where it is confined to the east and south coasts and their vicinity, the Brown Tail is found all round the Essex littoral. Periodically it attains abundance in certain localities, chiefly along the Thames estuary and notably on Canvey Island, where its larvae cause tremendous damage to vegetation. It is, however, also found some distance inland: in the north-east it is common in some years on the west side of Colchester at Lexden and along the Colne Valley (JF) and it occurred at Aldham in 1971 (MRSM); in east-central Essex it is found sparingly on Danbury Ridge (GAP); and towards the south it is common at Thorndon Park/Ingrave (PCF, KWG) and is found in small numbers at Doddinghurst (JTS) and Coxtie Green (PJW). It was noted in the south-west at Loughton in 1934 (*Lond. Nat.*, 33:125); in the extreme north at Lamarsh in 1970 (FDB:CNHS); and also during the last decade in such widely scattered inland localities as Epping, Ongar, Wickford and the Dunmow/Felsted areas. Its appearance well away from the coast may reflect a comparatively

recent, and perhaps still continuing, extension of range as no inland localities are mentioned in the older literature.

*Euproctis similis* Fuessl. (Gold Tail)
Common everywhere, although doubtfully as abundant as formerly.

*Arctornis l-nigrum* Müll. (Black V)
Six examples of this sizeable white moth, which is a very rare wanderer to the British Isles, occurred in an Essex locality in 1947, and one or more appeared there annually until 1960 (recorder's name withheld). The only other county record concerns a single specimen at Chelmsford in July 1904 (*Ent. Rec.*, 67: 213).

*Leucoma salicis* L. (White Satin)
Somewhat local, this fairly large glossy white species appears to be most prevalent today in parts of south-east Essex where, e.g., it is common in the built-up area of Westcliff-on-Sea (HCH) and at Thundersley (DGD). Well-known in the Metropolis it has been recorded frequently in the north-east suburbs and in 1934 was swarming on the poplars around Walthamstow Reservoirs (*Entomologist*, 67:237). Elsewhere in the southern half of Essex, as in the east and north-east, it is fairly widely distributed at generally low density, but it appears to be rare in west and north-west Essex. There, the only locality from which it has been reported is Hales Wood National N.R., Ashdon (RJR). The VCH considered it to be to some extent an immigrant, thousands having arrived from the sea at Harwich in 1878 when they were likened to a snowstorm, and there is subsequent evidence of migration in 1960 (only) when a total of *c*. 200 was recorded in June at Bradwell-on-Sea where normally only a few occur annually (AJD).

*Lymantria dispar* L. (Gipsy)
This species has been regarded as extinct in the British Isles for many years. Single males which occurred at Lexden, Colchester, on 10 July 1959 (JF) and at Mayland on 4 August 1971 (PCF) may well have been immigrants although the possibility that they were escaped or released specimens bred from continental stock cannot be ruled out.

*Lymantria monacha* L. (Black Arches)
Very local and scarce; not recorded during the past decade. The VCH referred to this most attractive moth as occurring frequently in oak woods, but records during the past 50 years are so few that they can be listed, viz.: Hatfield Forest, sparingly in 1933–34 (PBMA) and present 1945 (BSCNHS); Parndon, 1945 (*Essex Nat.*, 28:37); St. Osyth, 1948 (W. P. Seabrook coll.); Danbury Ridge, a male assembled to a bred female, 1950 (AJD, WPS); Wickham Bishops, a few *c*. 1950 (AJD); Westcliff-on-Sea, one in MV trap, 2 September 1958 (HCH); Ongar, one, 12–13 August 1958 (DCT); Hadleigh, one, 3 August 1960 (DGD). There are several 19th

century records from Epping Forest and district, but none since.

*Malacosoma neustria* L. (Lackey)
Generally distributed and common. Numbers tend to fluctuate from year to year and periodically it approaches abundance, at least in the larval web stage, in some localities.

*Malacosoma castrensis* L. (Ground Lackey)
Widely distributed on the coast. The south Suffolk, Essex and north Kent coasts and estuaries comprise the British home of this species. In Essex it is recorded from the more extensive and remote saltings at many points from Harwich round to Benfleet, but it no longer occurs in the latter area or at Leigh-on-Sea (HCH). While it is well represented in a number of other localities, Hamford Water, Colne Point and the Crouch estuary (inland as far as Hullbridge) appear to be its strongholds.

*Trichiura crataegi* L. (Pale Eggar)
Fairly widespread; not common. The VCH regarded this diminutive eggar as generally distributed but nowhere common. Today it appears to be less widespread although it has been noted in recent years in a number of widely scattered localities, in most of which it seems to occur only at low density.

*Poecilocampa populi* L. (December Moth)
This species, which, despite its name, is seen more often in November than December, is generally distributed and occurs at quite high density in many areas.

*Eriogaster lanestris* L. (Small Eggar)
This is a very local species and seems virtually to be confined to south-east Essex from the north bank of the Crouch estuary southwards. Even within this area it is prone to disappear for lengthy periods: thus it was apparently absent from the Rochford Hundred from 1920–30 and has not been seen there since 1970 (HCH). It has been plentiful at times on Canvey Island where, e.g., 'a good number' of larvae were found in 1959 (*Ent. Rec.*, 72:10). In the north of this area odd nests of larvae are at present to be found annually at Burnham-on-Crouch (DGD), and two nests were seen at Althorne in 1968 (RRC). The only other Essex records in recent times concern single specimens at Bradwell-on-Sea in 1952 and 1954 (AJD) and a nest of larvae found in June 1957 at East Donyland near Colchester (JF).

*Lasiocampa quercus* L. (Oak Eggar)
This fine moth is still widely distributed but has decreased and is now scarce in many areas where it was formerly common. Dr. C. G. M. de Worms noted as long ago as 1953 that it seemed to have become distinctly scarcer around London (*Lond. Nat.*, 33: 128) and the start of the decline in Essex as a whole probably dates from the same period, i.e., the late 1940s. Loss of suitable habitats to building or agriculture; lack of woodland management; en-

croachment of rank vegetation (or, conversely, too frequent mowing) in the open spaces in which this species delights; and crop-spraying have probably all contributed to its growing scarcity. Today it is probably more prevalent in grassy places on or near the coast, such as Fingringhoe Wick N.R. (SEL, GAP) and the Hadleigh/Benfleet downs (DGD, HCH) than elsewhere in the county.

*Macrothylacia rubi* L. (Fox Moth)
The remarks concerning the last species apply in large measure to the present one, except that it is less widely distributed. More dependent than the Oak Eggar on extensive areas of heathland or other uncultivated ground, it is distinctly coast-oriented in Essex, and inland is largely confined to wide expanses of rough ground which still exist in the Ministry of Defence lands south of Colchester, on Danbury Ridge, and around Brentwood. It appears to be absent from west Essex.

*Philudoria potatoria* L. (Drinker)
Generally distributed and common, especially in lush, grassy areas and marshes.

*Gastropacha quercifolia* L. (Lappet)
The VCH stated that this large moth, with its rich purplish-brown colouration, was generally distributed but far from common. This accurately describes its present Essex status.

*Saturnia pavonia* L. (Emperor)
As in the case of *L. quercus* (above) this striking moth, with its equally conspicuous larva, is widely distributed but has been declining for a number of years. Like the Oak Eggar it is generally to be found at low density in inland localities nowadays, but it is still fairly common on parts of the coast such as The Naze (JKW) and the Hadleigh/Benfleet downs (DGD, HCH).

*Drepana binaria* Hufn. (Oak Hook-tip)
Widely distributed, this attractive little moth is fairly common in most well-wooded localities and is also found at low density in a number of less well timbered districts where the oak is represented.

*Drepana cultraria* F. (Barred Hook-tip)
Very local. This beech-feeder, which is sometimes called the Beech Hook-tip, has long been known to occur plentifully in Epping Forest and may well still do so, although the only recent record dates back to 1960 (HEC). It is found sparingly in the Brentwood area at Ingrave (KWG) and Thorndon Park (RRC, PCF), and around Colchester at Lexden, Birch and Layer-de-la-Haye (JF). The only other records relate to a larva beaten at Ugley in the west in 1935 (PBMA), and single specimens on Danbury Ridge on 26 August 1967 (GAP) and at Bradwell-on-Sea on 9 August 1971 (AJD).

*Drepana falcataria* L. (Pebble Hook-tip)
This attractive moth is widely distributed; common in birch woods,

it is probably to be found in most places where that tree is well represented.

*Drepana lacertinaria* L. (Scalloped Hook-tip)
The status of this species, also a birch feeder, is similar to that of the last, except that it is perhaps not so widely distributed and is less common in some of its localities.

*Cilix glaucata* Scop. (Chinese Character)
This small whitish species, which so closely resembles a bird dropping when at rest, is generally distributed. Although it is still common or fairly so through most of its range the statement in the VCH that it abounds everywhere certainly does not apply today.

*Nola cucullatella* L. (Short-cloaked)
Far and away the most widespread and numerous of this family of tiny moths occurring in Essex, the present species is generally distributed and common in many districts.

*Nola strigula* Schiff. (Small Black Arches)
Very rare. Possibly extinct. The VCH gave several localities for this species, but in comparatively recent years it has been noted in only one of them, namely Belfairs, Hadleigh, where it was last seen in 1934 (HCH).

*Nola albula* Schiff. (Kent Black Arches)
Noted (as a migrant) only at Bradwell-on-Sea where it has occurred in ten years between 1949 and 1973 inclusive (AJD).

*Celama confusalis* H-S. (Least Black Arches)
Extremely local, it has been reported most frequently and in some numbers from Epping Forest, most recently on 2 May 1948 (*Proc. S. Lond. ent. nat. Hist. Soc.*, 1948–9: 69). Elsewhere it has occurred only at Benfleet and Hadleigh, where it was annual but rare up to 1939 (HCH), and singly in Hatfield Forest in 1949 (GD), at Lexden, Colchester, in June 1957 (JF), and at Bradwell-on-Sea on 19 May 1970 (AJD).

*Celama trituberculana* Bosc (Scarce Black Arches)
The first example of this migrant species to have been recorded in Essex was taken towards the west of the county at Parndon in 1945 (*Essex Nat.*, 28:37). Subsequent records are all from Bradwell-on-Sea—in 1956, 1957 (3) and 1963 (AJD).

*Atolmis rubricollis* L. (Red-necked Footman)
Rare. The VCH cited various localities for this species in the Tendring Hundred but there is no evidence that it is now resident anywhere in Essex. However, single wanderers were recorded at light at Bradwell-on-Sea in 1951 and 1952 (AJD).

*Nudaria mundana* L. (Muslin Footman)
Very local. The VCH gave but three localities for it, and in more recent years it has been recorded from only three areas—near Colchester at Lexden, High Woods and Berechurch (JF); at

48

Bradwell-on-Sea almost annually (AJD); and in a restricted locality near Rochford up to 1960 (HCH).

*Comacla senex* Hübn. (Round-winged Muslin Footman)
Apparently very local. Reported from few localities up to the turn of the century, and the only recent records that can be traced are: Bradwell-on-Sea, occurs most years (AJD); near Rochford, thinly distributed in one restricted locality up to 1960 (HCH); Hatfield Forest, 28 July 1969 (GHBS); Danbury Ridge and Chelmer Valley N.R., Little Baddow, occurs sparingly (GAP); Alder Carr N.R., Little Waltham, July 1971 (GAP); Thorndon Park, 25 June 1973 (PCF); Skipper's Island N.R., Hamford Water, 7–8 July 1973 (DGD).

*Miltochrista miniata* Forst. (Rosy Footman)
This delightful little moth is widespread in well-wooded areas in which oak is well represented, but it is apparently absent from the extreme west of the county and has not been reported from the Epping Forest area since the turn of the century, though it may well still occur there.

*Cybosia mesomella* L. (Four-dotted Footman)
Very local and scarce. This species was stated by the VCH to be widely distributed, although not common, but it has declined along with tracts of heather: its larvae feed on algae which grow on this plant. It is now very local and is known to occur, in small numbers, only on Danbury Ridge (DGD, GAP) and at Thorndon Park/Ingrave (PCF, KWG). Two were noted in Norsey Wood, Billericay, on 6 July 1941 (EFW) and it was last seen at Hadleigh in 1959 in a locality now built over (HCH) but it has not been reported from other relict heathland for many years, although it may possibly still survive at low density here and there. Wanderers occurred at Bradwell-on-Sea in 1961, 1968 and 1969 (AJD).

*Lithosia quadra* L. (Large Footman)
Known in Essex as a rare migrant, this moth, sometimes called the Four-spotted Footman, is by far the largest member of its family found in the British Isles. It has occurred as an irregular visitor over many years but apart from one at Westcliff-on-Sea in 1953 (HCH) all records since 1949 come from Bradwell-on-Sea where three occurred in 1950, 14 in 1951 and singles in four years between 1957 and 1965 inclusive (AJD).

*Eilema deplana* Esp. (Buff Footman)
A single specimen on Danbury Ridge on 23 July 1972 (GAP) is the sole Essex occurrence, apart from a very old record of one in Epping Forest *c*. 1870 (*Essex Nat.*, 158).

*Eilema griseola* Hübn. (Dingy Footman)
Local. According to the VCH this footman of marshy localities and damp places in woods occurred frequently in many places at the turn of the century, but nowadays it is decidedly local. In east-central Essex it is widely distributed at low density on Danbury

Ridge and is found sparingly in the Chelmer Valley N.R., Little Baddow (GAP); in the east it is common at Bradwell-on-Sea (AJD) and was noted at Mayland on 2 August 1971 (PCF) and at Creeksea (2) on 25 July 1962 (DGD). In the south-east and south it is very scarce and local at Canewdon and Rochford (HCH), while one was found on Thames-side on 31 July 1967 (RT) and in south-central Essex it is scarce at Thorndon Park (PCF). The only recent records for north and north-east Essex concern one at Great Maplestead (BWJP) and occasional specimens at Dovercourt (MEA), while it is apparently absent from west Essex, though there are 19th century records from Epping Forest. The most distinct yellowish form, *stramineola* Doubl., which is predominant in some parts of Britain and was formerly found at Epping and Harwich (VCH), occurs occasionally at Bradwell-on-Sea (AJD) but does not seem to have been encountered elsewhere.

*Eilema lurideola* Zinck (Common Footman)

The most widespread of the Essex footmen: generally distributed and quite common in a number of localities.

*Eilema complana* L. (Scarce Footman)

Said to favour heathy areas and coast sands, this footman, which closely resembles the last species, is decidedly more local than *E. lurideola*. Records suggest that it is largely confined to the south, centre and east of the county and to the vicinity of the coast. The only record from the west comes from Takeley in 1973 (GHBS). It is usually much more common than *lurideola* on the gravels of Danbury Ridge (GAP); common generally in the Rochford Hundred (HCH); recorded from Wickham Bishops (GCD); found sparingly along Thames-side (RT); and at least as prevalent as *lurideola* at Thorndon Park/Ingrave (PCF, KWG). On the coast and estuaries to the north of the Crouch estuary it is common at Bradwell-on-Sea (AJD) and is recorded from Mayland (PCF), Colne Point N.R. (FDB), Skipper's Island N.R., Hamford Water (DGD, GAP), Wix (RM) and Dovercourt (MEA).

*Eilema pygmaeola* Doubl. (Pigmy Footman)

Examples of this exceedingly local British species were taken at light at Bradwell-on-Sea on 20 August 1958 and 11 August 1961 (AJD).

*Eilema sororcula* Hufn. (Orange Footman)

Extremely local. The Essex stronghold of this footman is to be found in the oak/ash woodland around Colchester: there it is said to be not uncommon in some years in High Woods (Colchester), Berechurch, East Donyland and West Bergholt (JF). Single specimens were noted at Benfleet and Hadleigh in June 1935 in woods which are no longer suitable for it (HCH) and at Dovercourt in May 1967 (MEA), but apart from 19th century records from Epping Forest and Hazeleigh, near Maldon, it has not been noted elsewhere in the county.

*Pelosia muscerda* Hufn. (Dotted Footman)
The only Essex records of this species come from Bradwell-on-Sea, the dates being 6 July 1957, 26 July 1962, 3 August 1963 and 6 August 1970 (AJD).
*Utetheisa pulchella* L. (Crimson-speckled)
This beautiful southern species is a very rare migrant which occurred in Essex several times in the last century but has been noted only twice in the present one, viz., one at Clacton-on-Sea on 19 October 1921 (*Entomologist*, 54:292) and a female at a bathroom window in Southend-on-Sea on 20 September 1961 (Dr. Morley *per* HCH).
*Callimorpha jacobaeae* L. (Cinnabar)
Widespread. The VCH stated that this colourful day-flier was to be found sparingly in many places, but was well established and common in only a few of them. Much the same could be said of it today: although some colonies have been obliterated by development, ploughing up or human pressure, others have become established, not least as a result of the proliferation of gravel workings. If anything the species is now perhaps more widespread than earlier this century, though nowhere really abundant. It is as well represented on the coast as anywhere and its conspicuous yellow and black larvae on *Senecio jacobaea* (Ragwort) are a familiar sight at such places as The Naze and Fingringhoe Wick N.R.
*Spilosoma lubricipeda* L. (White Ermine)
Generally distributed and common.
*Spilosoma urticae* Esp. (Water Ermine)
Local and virtually confined to the vicinity of the coast and estuaries. Noted, mostly at low density, in recent years at Hamford Water (JBF); Little Clacton and Weeley (*Essex Nat.*, 31:111); Colne Point N.R., Brightlingsea, Thorington, Alresford, and Fingringhoe (JF); West Mersea (DAA, JF); East Mersea (*Essex Nat.*, 31:111); Bradwell-on-Sea (AJD); Mayland (PCF); Creeksea (DGD, HCH); Canewdon and Rochford (HCH); Southend-on-Sea (*Essex Nat.*, 28:138) and Thames-side (RT). The only inland record is of one in Thorndon Park on 25 June 1973 (PCF).
*Spilosoma lutea* Hufn. (Buff Ermine)
Generally distributed and common.
*Cycnia mendica* Clerck (Muslin Ermine)
Widespread. The status of this dainty moth does not seem to have altered much since the VCH stated that it was found sparingly throughout Essex. Perhaps more common on and near the coast than elsewhere, its density appears to be lowest on the west side of the county.
*Diacrisia sannio* L. (Clouded Buff)
Very rare; probably extinct in the county. The VCH gave Epping Forest, Eastwood, Brentwood and Colchester as localities, but

during the past half-century it has occurred only at Belfairs Wood, Hadleigh, where it was rare but of annual appearance up to 1939 (HCH), and at Bradwell-on-Sea on 20 June 1947 (AJD).

*Phragmatobia fuliginosa* L. (Ruby Tiger)
Widespread. The VCH described this small but attractive tiger moth as scarce and local and gave the Colchester district as its only known locality at the time. It must, therefore, rank as one of our increased species, a view shared by Dr. C. G. M. de Worms writing of the London area in 1953 (*London Nat.*, 33:135), as it is now widespread in the county, albeit mostly at low or fairly low density.

*Parasemia plantaginis* L. (Wood Tiger)
Very rare: probably extinct. The VCH gave this day-flier as formerly occurring in a St. Osyth wood, while it was reported from the Harwich area in 1911 (*Entomologist*, 45:178). More recently, however, it has been noted only in Belfairs Wood, Hadleigh, where it was found in small numbers up to 1939 but only once (in 1948) since the last war (HCH).

*Arctia caja* L. (Garden Tiger)
This large and colourful species, with its well-known 'woolly bear' larva, is found in all parts of the county and is generally common.

*Arctia villica* L. (Cream-spot Tiger)
A predominantly coastal species, this strikingly handsome moth is largely confined in Essex to the littoral and its vicinity. Recorded in many places from Mistley on the Stour estuary round to Dagenham on Thames-side, it is still quite common in a number of localities, although there is some evidence of a decrease in recent years. It does not generally extend far inland: immediately to the west of Colchester it is found at Lexden (JF) and Stanway (*Essex Nat.*, 31:112); in the east it extends up the Blackwater estuary to Maldon (GAP); and in the south to Ramsden Bellhouse (PF) and North Ockendon (DCT). Three occurred at Ingrave between 1965 and 1967 (KWG) and a worn (undated) specimen at Stondon Massey nr. Ongar (DCT), its furthest penetration inland in recent times. Harwich is the only locality from which the handsome ab. *wardi* Mathew has been recorded (HBDK, GFM).

*Apoda avellana* L. (Festoon)
This diminutive and extremely local species has been found in only two localities, both near Colchester, this century. These are Lexden Park and Donyland Woods where it was recorded regularly from 1956 to 1962 (JF).

*Zygaena trifolii* Esp. (Broad-bordered Five-spot Burnet)
Local. Colonies of this burnet moth have been reported in recent years from Brightlingsea, Berechurch and West Bergholt (JF) and Dovercourt (MEA) in the north-east; Alder Carr N.R., Little Waltham (RWB); Ingrave (KWG); Epping Forest (*Proc. S. Lond. ent.*

*nat. Hist. Soc.*, 1947–8:64); and Hatfield Forest (PBMA).
*Zygaena lonicerae* Scheven (Narrow-bordered Five-spot Burnet)
Local. Most colonies of this species have been found well to the south in the county where it is common locally in the Rochford Hundred (DGD, HCH) and on Thames-side (RT) and has been noted in Grays Chalk Quarry N.R. (GAP). Elsewhere a strong colony exists in the Dengie Peninsula (AJD) and it is reported from Ingrave (KWG), Hatfield Forest (BSCNHS) and Skipper's Island N.R., Hamford Water (DGD).
*Zygaena filipendulae* L. (Six-spot Burnet)
Far and away the most widespread of the Essex members of this day-flying family, this species is to be found in colonies of varying size, but nowadays mostly small, on uncultivated ground in most localities where suitable habitats have so far survived the demands of development or intensive farming.
*Procris statices* L. (Common Forester)
Extremely local and rare. This delightful little translucent-winged greenish moth, also a day-flier, was common in Epping Forest in the last century (see, e.g., *Entomologist*, 18:90) but has been represented during the last 50 years only by single specimens at Hadleigh on 16 May 1947 (DGD) and in a locality near Brentwood in 1970 (on the extremely late date of 12 July) and again in 1971 (KWG).

A word of explanation is necessary in the case of the next family to be considered, the *Sesiidae* or 'clearwings'. These moths are all day-flying and are rarely seen once they have flown off after drying their wings on emergence. As the majority of students of the Macro-lepidoptera lack specialist knowledge of the earlier life stages of members of this family, without which they are unable—except by accident—to locate the various species in their respective localities, the status of clearwings is unknown in many places and only imperfectly known in others. Consequently the information given below must be regarded as in all cases incomplete, and in most only fragmentary.
*Sesia apiformis* Clerck (Poplar Hornet Clearwing)
Even at the turn of the century this species was said to be declining due to the felling of poplars (VCH) and no doubt this trend has continued. In 1955 it was still described as common in parts of south-east Essex (HCH) but it is now much more local and scarce in that area due to the widespread destruction of host trees, as at Westcliff-on-Sea (DGD, HCH). Although it must have occurred at one time, and possibly still does, over much of the county, the only other localities in which it has been recorded in recent years are Ramsden Bellhouse where a colony still exists (PF); Colchester (Ipswich Road) where DC frequently saw specimens 'sunning them-

selves' at the base of black poplars in his garden in the 1940s and early 1950s but not after 1958; and Dovercourt in 1932 (HEC) and 1964 (MEA).

*Sphecia bembeciformis* Hübn. (Osier Hornet Clearwing)

The VCH stated that this insect, sometimes known as the Lunar Hornet Clearwing, occurred everywhere where sallow and osiers abounded, but except that it is still common at Hadleigh, present at Benfleet, and recorded from Rettendon (HCH), information regarding its present status is lacking. The only other recent records are of two imagines in Hatfield Forest on 20 July 1947 (*Ent. Rec.*, 79:155–156) and a 'colony' of larvae found in sallows during clearing operations at Fingringhoe Wick N.R. on 22 February 1970 (ENT).

*Aegeria andrenaeformis* Lasp. (Orange-tailed Clearwing)

'Mines' of this species in *Virburnum lantana* (Wayfaring tree) were found at Saffron Walden in 1955 (HCH; *Entomologist*, 88:198) and again in 1960 and 1961 (AME) but not subsequently. These are the only Essex records.

*Aegeria tipuliformis* Clerck (Currant Clearwing)

Currant being the larval food-plant this is predominantly a garden species. The VCH described it as common, and although the trend is for less intensively cultivated gardens, it is doubtless still quite prevalent in a number of districts as is the case in south-east Essex (DGD, HCH) and at Lexden, Colchester, where, however, it has been less frequent since 1960 (JF). Elsewhere it has been reported during the last half-century only from the south-west at Forest Gate and Buckhurst Hill (*London Nat.*, 33:145) and from Writtle Agricultural College (Writtle Ag. Coll. coll.).

*Aegeria vespiformis* L. (Yellow-legged Clearwing)

The VCH stated that this clearwing was to be found everywhere in oak stumps where the trees had been felled the previous year. All that can be said of its present-day status is that it is still common locally in south-east Essex where larvae have also been found on poplar (HCH), while larvae were found at Debden in 1967 and 1968 (AME) and four drowned imagines in a garden pond at Tiptree on 2 August 1971 (FDB).

*Aegeria myopaeformis* Borkh. (Small Red-belted Clearwing)

The VCH described this species, which is a frequenter of gardens and orchards, as 'probably the greatest enemy of the apple grower that exists'. No doubt the intensive spraying of fruit trees has had its effect, although it is still prevalent in old gardens and orchards in south-east Essex (HCH). Elsewhere it has been recorded in recent years only in the Ongar area (DCT).

*Aegeria culiciformis* L. (Large Red-Belted Clearwing)

According to the VCH it probably occurred at the turn of the century in all birch woods, but the only recent records come from south-east Essex, in parts of which it is still common (HCH), and Weeley, in the north-east, where pupae were found *c.* 1950 (Dr. E. B. Ford, S. Beaufoy *per* HEC).

*Aegeria formicaeformis* Esp. (Red-tipped Clearwing)
On the authority of the VCH, at the turn of the century this clearwing was local and less frequent than when osiers had been more extensively cultivated. The only subsequent records come from south-east Essex where it occurred sparsely in one area up to 1947 (HCH) and Thames-side where several imagines were seen on 26 June 1972 (GG) and one on 20 June 1974 (GG, BS).

*Dipsosphecia scopigera* Scop. (Six-belted Clearwing)
Formerly common locally in south-east Essex, it is now confined to one restricted area (HCH). Apart from an old record of one at Hazeleigh near Maldon in 1874 (*Essex Field Club Trans.*, 3:39) it has not been noted elsewhere in the county.

*Zeuzera pyrina* L. (Wood Leopard)
The VCH described this blue-black spotted white moth as far from common generally but occurring sparingly in many places. Much the same can be said of it today, but although it remains fairly common in some areas such as Westcliff and Leigh-on-Sea (HCH) it has become scarcer in others in recent years.

*Cossus cossus* L. (Goat Moth)
Much declined. Even at the turn of the century there were signs that this large species, though still common, was declining due to the removal of large numbers of infested trees (VCH). This decline has accelerated since the 1939–45 war in pace with the wholesale destruction of unhealthy trees. It is now scarce in most areas and may even have become extinct in some. Here and there, as at Ramsden Bellhouse (PF), small pockets remain where infested trees have not been removed, but even in some of the most extensively timbered districts of the county it now appears only occasionally if at all.

*Hepialus humuli* L. (Ghost Moth)
Generally distributed and common.

*Hepialus sylvina* L. (Wood Swift)
Widely distributed, this moth, alternatively known as the Orange Swift, is fairly common in a number of localities.

*Hepialus lupulina* L. (Common Swift)
Very common everywhere, abounding in some localities.

*Hepialus hecta* L. (Golden Swift)
Local. The larva of this species feeds exclusively on bracken: consequently it is less widespread than any of the other swifts occurring in Essex, though to be found in most localities where its foodplant flourishes. In such places it can be very common.

*Actinotia polyodon* Clerck (Purple Cloud)
Two examples of this wanderer to the British Isles from the con-

tinent have been taken at light at Bradwell-on-Sea, one on 27 May 1954 and the other on 16 May 1960 (AJD).

*Euxoa nigricans* L. (Garden Dart)

Widely, perhaps generally, distributed at varying density.

*Euxoa tritici* L. (White-line Dart)

Almost exclusively a coastal species in Essex, this moth has been noted in a number of sea-board and estuarine localities from Manningtree round to Rainham on Thames-side, in some of which it is quite common. Apart from one or two records from the Metropolitan area in the last century, it has not occurred at any distance inland, odd examples in the 1960s at North Ockendon (DCT) representing the furthest penetration from the coast.

*Agrotis segetum* Schiff. (Turnip Moth)

Generally distributed and common, approaching abundance at times in areas where root crops are grown extensively.

*Agrotis vestigialis* Hufn. (Archer's Dart)

Very local. The VCH stated that this species was found uncommonly on the coast sands: Shoeburyness and Westcliff-on-Sea are specifically mentioned in the 19th century literature. Two were obtained in the Harwich area in 1911 (*Entomologist*, 45:266) and the only subsequent records are: Dovercourt, 17 August 1935 (HEC); Bradwell-on-Sea, 29 August 1963 and 3 August 1971 (AJD); Colne Point N.R., two, 11 August 1973 (DGD *et al.*).

*Agrotis clavis* Hufn. (Heart and Club)

Fairly widespread; not common. This species is known to occur in a number of localities scattered throughout the county, almost invariably at low or fairly low density. Due to its close resemblance to the very common *A. exclamationis* (below) it may be overlooked in some districts and could prove to be more widely distributed and less sparse than at present seems the case.

*Agrotis puta* Hübn. (Shuttle-shaped Dart)

Generally distributed and common.

*Agrotis exclamationis* L. (Heart and Dart)

Very common everywhere.

*Agrotis ipsilon* Hufn. (Dark Sword-grass)

This moth, also known as the Dark Dart, is one of those species whose native population is swollen by immigrants. Consequently it fluctuates widely in numbers from year to year and although as a rule it is generally distributed there are some years when it is almost or entirely absent from certain districts, yet in others it is well-represented and sometimes very common.

*Agrotis ripae* Hübn. (Sand Dart)

Very local. The VCH indicated that it was confined to the coast sands between Harwich and St. Osyth and this still appears to be the case. It was noted in the Harwich/Dovercourt area in 1936

(HEC), 1937 (*Entomologist*, 71:183) and 1938 (*Entomologist*, 72: 261), while larvae were found in numbers at the Naze in 1959 (*Ent. Rec.*, 72:10) and JF confirms it is still present in both these localities as well as at Colne Point N.R., St. Osyth, where it was also recorded, in 1974, by RCH.

*Lychophotia varia* Vill. (True Lover's Knot)
As would be expected this most attractive and quaintly named little moth is local, but considering the extent to which its food-plant, heather, has declined it has been noted in late years in a surprising number of localities: probably it subsists on garden heathers in some districts. It is still quite numerous locally in the Brentwood area (PCF, KWG) and on Danbury Ridge (GAP), and is found in small numbers in the south-east at Westcliff/Leigh-on-Sea and Hadleigh (HCH) and at Thundersley (DGD). Additionally it has been noted during the past decade at Ongar where it occurs sparingly (DCT); at Dovercourt (MEA) and Bradwell-on-Sea (AJD) in 1969; at Coxtie Green in 1971 (PJW); at Hamford Water in 1972 (JBF); and in Epping Forest in 1974 (NA).

*Peridroma porphyrea* Schiff. (Pearly Underwing)
The remarks made in the case of *Agrotis ipsilon* (above) apply to the present species except that it is generally a much less numerous insect. In most years it occurs only at low density and fails to appear at all in some districts. Periodically, however, its numbers are heavily reinforced by immigrants and on such occasions it can become widespread and common.

*Rhyacia simulans* Hufn. (Dotted Rustic)
Intentionally or otherwise the VCH failed to mention a record of 'several at sugar' at Stansted Mountfitchet in 1875 (*Entomologist*, 1: 155). There is but one other record of this sizeable noctuid, one having occurred near Coxtie Green on 26 July 1974 (PJW).

*Spaelotis ravida* Schiff. (Stout Dart)
Irregular. This species, although rarely common and then only locally, periodically becomes fairly widespread for a few years. At other times it is absent from the county or seemingly so. The most likely explanation seems to be that it is an irregular immi-grant which, from time to time, establishes itself temporarily. R. F. Bretherton (*Ent. Gaz.*, 8:3–19; 195–198) has shown that south Essex is one of its principal localities in Great Britain and that it seems to favour the edges of marshland.

Evidently there was a sizeable influx in 1936 as several were seen in north-east Essex (*Entomologist*, 70:87) and it was also reported from Loughton (*London Nat.*, 34:74) and described as abundant even as far to the north-west as Manuden (PBMA). It was also much in evidence, at least in south-east Essex, in 1950 (HCH) and in the late 1950s, no fewer than 20 having been recorded at Bradwell-on-Sea in 1958 (AJD). It has been recorded annually since 1963 and for the past few years has occurred at mainly low density in a number of localities scattered throughout the county.

*Graphiphora augur* Fab. (Double Dart)

Generally distributed and not uncommon in many localities.

*Diarsia brunnea* Schiff. (Purple Clay)

The VCH stated that this moth was common in woods and it is still quite widespread and reasonably represented in well-timbered localities, except that it appears to be rare (or, perhaps, under-recorded) in west Essex, Birchanger being the only locality from which it has been reported (CSC, CM). There are no records from Epping Forest and district this century, although it would be surprising if it did not still occur there.

*Diarsia mendica* F. (Common Ingrailed Clay)

This attractive and variable species is also predominantly a woodland insect. It is more widespread and at the same time much more common than *D. brunnea*, and is sometimes very numerous in some of the more heavily wooded areas.

*Diarsia dahlii* Hübn. (Barred Chestnut)

Extremely local and scarce. The VCH stated that it had been recorded as occurring in the county by J. W. Tutt, but gave no details. The only other records are: Hadleigh/Benfleet, small numbers in two woods from 1934–39 (HCH); Danbury Ridge, occurs almost annually at low density (GAP).

*Diarsia rubi* View. (Small Square-spot)

Generally distributed and common.

*Ochropleura plecta* L. (Flame Shoulder)

Generally distributed and common.

*Amathes glareosa* Esp. (Autumnal Rustic)

Decidedly local. This delicately marked woodland species was recorded by the VCH from Epping, Woodford, Brentwood and, occasionally, Colchester. More recently it has been reported from the following places: Brentwood district, locally common in South Weald Park (RRC) and common in some seasons at Thorndon Park/Ingrave (PCF, KWG); Stondon Massey, occasional specimens (DCT); Danbury Ridge, widespread and locally common (GAP); Langdon Hills, small numbers (RT); Wickham Bishops (GCD).

*Amathes castanea* Esp. (Neglected Rustic)

There are only three Essex records of this heathland species, alternatively known as the Grey Rustic. One was from Wanstead Flats in July 1879 (*Entomologist*, 12:165), the next from Danbury Ridge on 13 August 1935 (GAP) and the third from Coxtie Green on 28 August 1971 (PJW). The last was a specimen of the reddish form which suggests that it may have been a wanderer from the southern heathlands.

*Amathes baja* Schiff. (Dotted Clay)

Widely distributed at varying density in well-timbered districts.

*Amathes c-nigrum* L. (Setaceous Hebrew Character)
Common everywhere, frequently approaching abundance in the late summer. Pale or albinistic forms have been taken at Bradwell-on-Sea (AJD).

*Amathes ditrapezium* Schiff. (Triple-spotted Clay)
Very local. Brentwood was the only locality given for this species in the VCH. However, it was noted in Birchanger Wood in 1920 (CSC) and at Benfleet (2) in 1935 (HCH), while it is found in two localities near Brentwood (RRC, PCF) and in a restricted locality (and occasionally elsewhere) on Danbury Ridge (DGD, GAP). It occurred at Bradwell-on-Sea in 1964 and 1970 (AJD). As it bears a strong resemblance to the larger and more strongly coloured examples of *A. triangulum* (below) it is possible that it may occasionally have been overlooked.

*Amathes triangulum* Hufn. (Double Square-spot)
Generally distributed and common.

*Amathes stigmatica* Hübn. (Square-spotted Clay)
Very local and rare. The VCH described it as decidedly scarce but widely distributed, yet occurrences at Loughton in 1879 (*Entomologist*, 12:234) and near Harwich in 1911 (*Entomologist*, 45:228) appear to be the only earlier published records. Apart from an undated occurrence at Manuden (PBMA), it has been noted subsequently only at Benfleet, where 2–3 were seen annually up to 1938 (HCH), and at Bradwell-on-Sea (1) on 17 August 1965 (AJD). It is possible that it has been overlooked on occasion as it bears a marked resemblance to some examples of both *Diarsia brunnea* and *A. triangulum* (above).

*Amathes sexstrigata* Haw. (Six-striped Rustic)
Widespread. The present status of this moth, which bears some resemblance to *Diarsia rubi* (above) and shows a preference for damp localities, seems to differ little from that given in the VCH, which stated that it was widely distributed but not very common. The number of localities, scattered throughout the county, in which it has been noted in recent years are too numerous to mention, but in all districts from which detailed information about its numbers has been received its density seems to be quite low in most years, and this may well prove to be the position over the county as a whole.

*Amathes xanthographa* Schiff. (Square-spot Rustic)
Very common everywhere and abundant in some districts.

*Axylia putris* L. (Flame Rustic)
Generally distributed and common in many localities.

*Anaplectoides prasina* Schiff. (Green Arches)
Always very local and scarce, this beautiful noctuid had been recorded up to the turn of the century from Epping, Warley and Colchester (VCH). Subsequent records are extremely few: 1–2 in

two Benfleet/Hadleigh Woods in June 1935 (HCH); Lexden, Colchester, June 1959 (JF); Bradwell-on-Sea, occurred in five years between 1952 and 1969 inclusive (AJD); Hadleigh, June 1968 (D. Smith *per* HCH); Takeley, July 1973 and 1974 (GHBS).

*Eurois occulta* L. (Great Brocade)
In southern England this magnificent noctuid occurs as a scarce and irregular immigrant from the continent. The more recent Essex records are: three at Bradwell-on-Sea, July/August 1954 (AJD); 14 there (AJD) and four at Westcliff-on-Sea (HCH), July/ August 1955; three at Bradwell-on-Sea (AJD) and single specimens at Westcliff-on-Sea and Rowhedge (*Proc. Ent. Soc.*, 5:113–114) in August 1959; nine at Bradwell-on-Sea (AJD) and one at Ongar (DCT) in August 1964; singly at Benfleet (JEC) and Langdon Hills (RT) in August 1972 and at Coxtie Green in July 1973 (PJW).

*Cerastis rubricosa* Schiff. (Red Chestnut)
Widespread. The VCH's statement that this reddish-brown species was nowhere numerous is still true. Widely, if not generally, distributed it seems to occur only at low or fairly low density.

*Naenia typica* L. (Gothic)
Widely distributed; much less common than formerly. The VCH described this species as common generally, but this is certainly not the case today. As far back as 1954 Dr. C. G. M. de Worms, apparently referring not only to the London area but to the country as a whole, stated that it was steadily becoming scarcer (*London Nat.*, 34:105), and while it could probably still be described as widespread in Essex, judging by recent status reports from a number of areas it is now extremely scarce in many districts and doubtfully numerous anywhere. Why this should be so is a mystery as the insect frequents areas containing rank herbage, of which there is no shortage.

*Euschesis comes* Hübn. (Lesser Yellow Underwing)
Common everywhere.

*Euschesis orbona* Hufn. (Lunar Yellow Underwing)
Rare. Although the VCH did not mention this species, which closely resembles the last, there are several 19th century records, mostly from the south-west, in the literature, and it was said to be fairly plentiful at Dovercourt in 1911 (*Entomologist*, 45:33). Otherwise there are fully authenticated records only from Chelmsford where it was taken from 1938–42 (W. P. Seabrook coll.) and of single specimens at Lexden (Colchester) in July 1959 and at West Bergholt in August 1960 (JF).

*Euschesis janthina* Schiff. (Lesser-bordered Yellow Underwing)
Generally distributed and common in many districts.

*Euschesis interjecta* Hübn. (Least Yellow Underwing)
Widespread. The VCH described this yellow underwing, the only day-flier of the genus, although it also flies by night, as widely

distributed but scarcer than formerly. It is still found over large areas of the undeveloped parts of the county and remains fairly numerous in suitable localities.

*Noctua pronuba* L. (Large Yellow Underwing)
Very common everywhere and often locally abundant.

*Lampria fimbriata* Schreber (Broad-bordered Yellow Underwing)
This most handsome insect is very widely distributed and is not uncommon in some districts. Generally regarded as a woodland species it is by no means confined to wooded areas, though it is usually scarce where it occurs in the more sparsely timbered localities.

*Pyrrhia umbra* Hufn. (Bordered Sallow)
Local and scarce. As indicated in the VCH this handsome species, alternatively known as the Bordered Orange, shows a distinct preference for the coast and its vicinity, although it has been recorded in several inland areas. South-east Essex, where it is locally not uncommon (DGD, HCH), seems to be its stronghold, while 1–2 appear in most years on Thames-side (RT). Further west it is occasional at Hornchurch and Plaistow (WLC). North of the Crouch estuary it is fairly regular but scarce at Bradwell-on-Sea (AJD) and one was noted at Mayland in 1971 (PCF). In the north-east there are records from Dovercourt in 1937 (HEC) and Hamford Water (JBF). It appears to be decidedly scarce inland. 1–2 appear in some years at Ingrave (KWG), it has been recorded in the Ongar area (DCT), and two were taken at Writtle in 1967 (Writtle Ag. Coll. coll.). Single specimens were noted on Danbury Ridge in 1967 (GAP), Hookend in 1971 (RRC) and near Takeley in 1972 (GHBS).

*Heliothis viriplaca* Hufn. (Marbled Clover)
The VCH reported that it had occurred on the north-east Essex coast. The only subsequent records concern individuals at Bradwell-on-Sea on 21 July 1951 and 7 July 1952 (AJD).

*Heliothis peltigera* Schiff. (Dark Bordered Straw)
This well-known migrant occurs in Essex irregularly and in small numbers. Six have been noted in recent years in south-east Essex (HCH) and it has been recorded in six years since 1951 at Bradwell-on-Sea with a maximum of four in 1958 (AJD). Away from the coast it has occurred, singly, during the past 50 years only at Collier Row, Romford, on 26 May 1966 (RRC) and Danbury Ridge in July 1967 (CH).

*Heliothis armigera* Hübn. (Scarce Bordered Straw)
Also a very scarce and irregular immigrant, *H. armigera* has occurred since 1925 only at: Westcliff-on-Sea, 8 July 1951 and 27 August 1955 (HCH); Bradwell-on-Sea, in eight years since 1950 when a maximum of three appeared (AJD); Hockley, 11 September 1957 (*Essex. Nat.*, 30:124); Thames-side, 10 October 1966 (RT); Ongar, 14 October 1969 (DCT).

*Mamestra brassicae* L. (Cabbage Moth)
Generally distributed and common or fairly so.

*Melanchra persicariae* L. (The Dot)
Also generally distributed and common in some years.

*Polia hepatica* Clerck (Silvery Arches)
Very rare; possibly extinct. The VCH stated that this attractive noctuid was scarce and local. Since then it has been found only at Hadleigh in 1935 and 1936 (HCH).

*Polia nitens* Haw. (Pale Shining Arches)
Rather local and uncommon generally. The VCH, while describing this moth as 'not uncommon', gave no indication of its range in Essex. Today it is known to occur in a good number of localities scattered throughout the county, although it is by no means generally distributed and as a rule is scarce. It seems to be most widespread in the south and south-east of the county and least in evidence in the west.

*Polia nebulosa* Hufn. (Grey Arches)
Widely distributed in well-timbered districts; not uncommon in some areas but sparse in others and doubtfully numerous anywhere.

*Diataraxia oleracea* L. (Bright-line Brown-eye)
Generally distributed and common. Melanic specimens are recorded from the Rochford Hundred (HCH).

*Ceramica pisi* L. (Broom Moth)
Widely distributed and common or fairly so in many districts.

*Hada nana* Hufn. (Shears)
Very widespread. The VCH stated that this well-patterned noctuid was of general occurrence and this is probably still the case as it has been recorded in recent years in most parts of the county. However, it is to be found only at low density in a number of districts and does not seem to be really numerous anywhere.

*Scotogramma trifolii* Hufn. (Small Nutmeg)
Generally distributed and common, approaching abundance locally in some years.

*Hadena w-latinum* Hufn. (Light Brocade)
Decidedly local. According to the VCH this attractive species, while even then far from common, was generally distributed at the turn of the century. At present, however, it appears to be extremely scarce and local away from south Essex. There it is described as common in the Rochford Hundred (HCH), while one was seen at Stanford-le-Hope on 26 May 1951 (*Proc. S. Lond. ent. nat. Hist. Soc.*, 1951–2:70), a total of five in Grays Chalk Quarry N.R. in 1968 and 1972 (RT), and one at Langdon Hills on 17 June 1973 (RT). Elsewhere it has been recorded during the last half century only from Bradwell-on-Sea up to 1964 (AJD) and from Ugley in 1935 (PBMA), Chelmsford in 1947 (W. P. Seabrook coll.) and near Takeley on 6 July 1972 (GHBS), all single specimens.

*Hadena suasa* Schiff. (Dog's Tooth)

Local. This moth is to be found in many places on and near the coast and estuaries from Harwich round to Tilbury. In some of the localities it is quite common and in the Rochford Hundred, where it is widely distributed, most specimens are now distinctly melanic (HCH). From Thames-side it extends north sparsely to the Brentwood area (*Lond. Nat.*, 34:85; KWG) but otherwise it has been noted away from the littoral only at Ugley in the north-west on 7 June 1936 (PBMA).

*Hadena thalassina* Hufn. (Pale-shouldered Brocade)

Rather local and scarce. The VCH gave this attractive noctuid as generally distributed and common: today it is rather local and occurs generally only at low density. Reported in recent years from some 18 localities scattered throughout the county it is mostly to be found in well-wooded districts.

*Hadena bicolorata* Hufn. (Broad-barred White)

Described by the VCH as generally common, this small white and grey-black noctuid is still widely distributed at varying density.

*Hadena conspersa* Schiff. (Common Marbled Coronet)

Rare. The VCH gave Epping as the only locality in which this attractively marked species had been taken. Subsequently occasional stragglers were noted on the Hadleigh/Benfleet downs up to 1937 (HCH) and one came to light at Clacton-on-Sea in July 1961 (JF). The only other recent record concerns three imagines reared at Saffron Walden in 1960 from larva found in *Silene vulgaris* (Bladder Campion) (AME) and it may yet prove to be established in the extreme north-west, as it is also found at Linton just over the county boundary with Cambridgeshire (RJR).

*Hadena compta* Schiff. (Varied Coronet)

Fairly widespread. Apart from a few 19th century occurrences this most attractive little grey-black and white noctuid was first noted in the British Isles in 1948 when several were taken in the Dover area flying around *Dianthus barbatus* (Sweet William). In the first week of July 1952 the first specimen to be recorded away from the Dover/Folkestone area was taken by DC at Colchester (*Ent. mon. Mag.*, 90:197) and in 1954 JF found many specimens on *D. barbatus* at a seed farm in the same district. It was first recorded in south-east Essex in 1957 (DGD). Since then the species has colonised extensive areas of Essex and is now distributed over much of the county and infilling rapidly. However, with the exception of one at Saffron Walden in 1960 (AME), there are as yet no records for the extreme west or north-west but this may be due to the paucity of recorders in that region.

*Hadena bicruris* Hufn. (Lychnis)

Generally distributed and common.

*Hadena rivularis* F. (Campion)

Local and scarce. The VCH gave this species, which closely resembles *H. bicruris*, as not uncommon. Today it is local and generally scarce. It was not uncommon at Benfleet up to at least 1964 (HCH) and was taken there in 1972 (JEC), a few occur in most years at Bradwell-on-Sea (AJD) and several were bred from larvae found at Saffron Walden in 1960 (AME). Odd specimens have been recorded in recent years at Dovercourt (MEA), Thames-side (RT), North Ockendon (DCT), Ingrave (KWG), Hookend (RRC), Ongar (DCT), Cranham (PCF) and Danbury Ridge (GAP).

*Hadena lepida* Esp. (Tawny Shears)

Decidedly local. The VCH described this *Silene* feeder as not uncommon but mentioned no localities for it. Today it is very local and scarce and all recent records can be cited: Chelmsford, two in 1934 (W. P. Seabrook coll.); Hadleigh/Benfleet Downs, several flying in sunshine annually from 1935 to 1939 (HCH); Farnham near Bishop's Stortford, series bred from larvae, 1941 (CC); Westcliff-on-Sea, one at light on 8 July 1956 was mottled dark brown, quite unlike the pale buff unicolorous or faintly marked specimens noted previously in that district (see above) and was probably an immigrant (HCH); Saffron Walden, series bred from larvae, 1960 (AME); Colne Point N.R., singly on 23 June 1960 (JF) and 11 August 1973 (DGD); Ongar, singly on 21 July 1962 and 24 June 1963 (DCT); Ingrave, 5 June 1963 (KWG); Bradwell-on-Sea, uncommon up to 1963, not noted since (AJD); Writtle, two in 1967 (Writtle Ag. Coll. coll.); Danbury Ridge, 7 May 1974 (GAP); Takeley, 1974 (GHBS).

*Hadena albicolon* Hübn. (White Colon)

Very local; apparently quite rare. The VCH stated that this maritime noctuid was 'sometimes found at Dovercourt and elsewhere on coast sands', although the only additional 19th century locality mentioned in the literature is Benfleet. It was recorded again in the Harwich district (i.e., Dovercourt) in 1911 (*Entomologist*, 45: 180). The only subsequent records, of single specimens, come from Colne Point N.R. in 1934 (larva) (HCH) and 23 June 1960 (JF, PB), Dovercourt on 9 and 18 June 1973 (MEA) and Bradwell-on-Sea on 3 June 1974 (AJD).

*Heliophobus reticulata* Vill. (Bordered Gothic)

Very local and scarce. The VCH recorded it as occurring sparingly in many places but the only subsequent records are: Westcliff-on-Sea, a few in 1953 and 1955 (HCH); Ongar, singly, 18 and 25 July 1962 (DCT); North Ockendon (3), 6 August 1963 (DCT); Bradwell-on-Sea, scarce and irregular up to 1966, since absent (AJD); Thames-side, 22 June 1967 (RT); Hookend, 1 July 1971 (RRC).

*Tholera popularis* F. (Feathered Gothic)

Widely distributed and common in a number of districts.

Gervase Mathew, the celebrated lepidopterist who gave his name to Mathew's Wainscot (*Leucania favicolor* Barr.). He caught the first British specimens on the saltings at Dovercourt in 1895. This photograph was taken near his home at Dovercourt in 1924, four years before his death, when he was 82.

A. J. Dewick (left) and J. Firmin examine moths inside the former's mercury vapour trap at Curry Farm, Bradwell-on-Sea. The trap, which has a catching chamber 11ft. square and 6ft. high, has attracted many migrant rarities including the first British specimen of *Plusia confusa* Steph. (Dewick's Plusia). Photo: G. B. Royffé

*Tholera cespitis* Schiff. (Hedge Rustic)
Local, not common. This species was described by the VCH as scarce and the same can still be said of it in general. It occurs in a number of localities in the eastern half of Essex and is generally found at low or very low density, but it is quite common in some years on Danbury Ridge (GAP). In recent years it has not been reported from further west than Mucking, the Brentwood district and Ongar, or from the north-west, but the paucity of observers may partly account for this.

*Cerapteryx graminis* L. (Antler)
Widespread. This grass feeder has probably declined in numbers since the VCH described it as common in many parts of the county, but it is still fairly widespread and is not uncommon in some districts, especially those where extensive areas of rough grassland still survive, such as Hatfield Forest, where it was described as 'abundant' in the 1940s (PBMA), and parts of the coast and estuary lands.

*Orthosia gothica* L. (Hebrew Character)
Very common everywhere.

*Orthosia miniosa* Schiff. (Blossom Underwing)
Local and scarce. This attractive quaker was described by the VCH as scarce but occurring in many oak woods. Today it remains scarce and is also decidedly local. All post-1925 records are given. In the south-east it is not uncommon at Benfleet, Hadleigh and Westcliff-on-Sea (HCH) and was noted at Thundersley in 1964 and 1969 (DGD). At Bradwell-on-Sea it was uncommon and irregular up to 1961 (AJD). In the north-east it was recorded at Weeley (larvae) in 1953 (HEC); Lexden (Colchester) and Donyland Woods in 1959 and 1960 (JF); Cannock Mill, Colchester, in April 1970 (FDB: CNHS) and Dovercourt (2) in May 1972 (MEA). There are a series of records of larvae from Warley, the latest *c.* 1950 (*Proc. S. Lond. ent. nat. Hist. Soc.*, 1949–50:74), and larvae were also found in a locality on Danbury Ridge in 1972 (DGD). In the west, larvae were found occasionally in Hatfield Forest from 1936–39 and it occurred in Canfield Hart Wood in 1946 (PBMA).

*Orthosia cruda* Schiff. (Small Quaker)
Generally distributed and common, approaching abundance in some districts.

*Orthosia stabilis* Schiff. (Common Quaker)
Very common everywhere.

*Orthosia populeti* F. (Lead-coloured Drab)
Local and generally scarce. The VCH stated that this sombre species was widespread among aspen but it is much less in evidence today: the only district in which it is known to be fairly common locally is Danbury Ridge (DGD, GAP). It is very scarce in the Rochford Hundred (DGD, HCH) and occurred at Bradwell-on-Sea only in 1955, 1957 and 1968 (AJD). In the Ongar area it was noted in

Ongar Park Woods in 1933 (*London Nat.*, 35:48) and is resident at low density at Ongar itself and Stondon Massey (DCT). It was also recorded at Quendon in 1962 (AME); near Brentwood at Ingrave (2) in 1965 (KWG) and Hookend in 1969 (RRC); and near Blackmore (2) in March 1974 (WLC). There are old records for Epping Forest and district from which it also recorded (without date) in the *London Naturalist* (35:48).

*Orthosia incerta* Hufn. (Clouded Drab)
Generally distributed and very common in infinite variety.

*Orthosia munda* Schiff. (Twin-spot Quaker)
Widely distributed among oak in small to moderate numbers.

*Orthosia advena* Schiff. (Northern Drab)
Very local: formerly rare but now established in south and east Essex and extending its range. The VCH gave this species as rare, mentioning Colchester (once), Southend-on-Sea and Wanstead as localities. Specimens were also taken near Brentwood in 1906 (*Entomologist*, 39:192). It persisted in the Southend area until 1939 (HCH) after which it was not recorded anywhere in the county until 1954 when it appeared at Bradwell-on-Sea where it has since been noted annually and is now fairly common (AJD). It has occurred in very small numbers at Westcliff-on-Sea since 1956 (HCH) while, immediately to the west, 1–2 were noted at Thundersley from 1968–70 (DGD) and five at Benfleet (JEC) and larvae at Leigh-on-Sea (DGD) in 1972. Single examples occurred annually on Thames-side from 1967–70 (RT), at Ingrave (KWG) and Coxtie Green (PJW) in May 1972, and at Ongar on 30 April 1973 (DCT).

*Orthosia gracilis* Schiff. (Powdered Quaker)
Generally distributed and common, or fairly so, in a number of districts.

*Panolis flammea* Schiff. (Pine Beauty)
Very local and scarce; possibly now beginning to establish itself. The VCH gave Birch, Colchester and Brentwood as localities for this beautiful reddish pine-feeder but it does not appear to have been recorded in Essex again until 1953 when three occurred at Hockley (DM). First taken at Bradwell-on-Sea in 1955 it appeared there again in 1964–65 and has occurred annually since 1969 (AJD). In the Colchester area two specimens were noted at Lexden in 1960 (JF) and single ones at Old Heath (JF) and Cannock Mill (FDB:CNHS) in 1970, the year in which two appeared at Hamford Water (JBF) and one at Hookend (RRC). It has appeared sparingly in some years at Ingrave (KWG) while one occurred at Writtle in 1967 (Writtle Ag. Coll. coll.) and two in 1972 and three in 1974 on Danbury Ridge (GAP).

*Meliana flammea* Curt. (Flame Wainscot)
A single specimen at Hamford Water on 24 May 1972 (JBF) is the only record.

*Leucania pallens* L. (Common Wainscot)
Very common everywhere.
*Leucania favicolor* Barr. (Mathew's Wainscot)
This extremely local insect, which is confined to eastern and southern England where its distribution is mainly coastal, was discovered by GFM at Dovercourt in 1895. It still occurs in the original locality (JF *et al.*) and has also been reported in recent years from The Naze N.R. (JF, JKW *et al.*); Colne Point N.R. (JF), Thorington Mill (FDB:CNHS), West Mersea (JF) and Bradwell-on-Sea (AJD) in the Colne/Blackwater estuary area; and from Creeksea (HCH, RRC), Hullbridge (HCH), Canewdon (HCH) and South Woodham (JEC, DGD) on the Crouch estuary. The only inland record is the surprising one of two specimens on waste ground by the busy Eastern Avenue, Ilford, in July 1954 (PB). Both abs. *rufa* Tutt and *aena* Mathew have been recorded.
*Leucania impura* Hübn. (Smoky Wainscot)
Generally distributed and common.
*Leucania straminea* Treits. (Southern Wainscot)
Local. The VCH described this wainscot, which resembles *L. impura*, as not common but occurring generally on the coast. There are also old records from Epping Forest and Tilbury (*London Nat.*, 35:37). In recent years it has occurred at low density on the coast and estuaries at Hamford Water (JBF), Bradwell-on-Sea (AJD), Rochford and Westcliff/Leigh-on-Sea (HCH), Benfleet (DGD) and on Thames-side (RT); but inland only in the Chelmer Valley N.R., Little Baddow (2) in July 1971 (GAP), at Thorndon Park (2) in 1973 (PCF) and once at Coxtie Green near Brentwood (PJW).
*Leucania pudorina* Schiff. (Striped Wainscot)
Very local and scarce. The VCH gave the Southend-on-Sea area as its only known locality but it has not been found there since. However, it occurs sparingly at Thorington, Rowhedge and West Mersea (JF) and was noted at Bradwell-on-Sea in 1952, 1957 and 1960 (AJD), while one was taken at Hamford Water on 16 July 1972 (JBF).
*Leucania obsoleta* Hübn. (Obscure Wainscot)
Local and scarce. Localities in which it was formerly noted are Southend, Rainham and Mucking (VCH) and 'near Tilbury' (*London Nat.*, 35:37). Recent records are: Westcliff/Leigh-on-Sea, very scarce (HCH); Bradwell-on-Sea from 1961–64 and in 1968 (AJD); North Ockendon, 10 June 1963 (DCT); Benfleet, 6 July 1972 (JEC); Thames-side, small to moderate numbers (RT); Ingrave/Thorndon Park, 1–2 in some years (WLC, KWG); Chelmer Valley N.R., Little Baddow (3), 21 June 1974 (GAP).
*Leucania litoralis* Curt. (Shore Wainscot)
Extremely local and apparently very rare. Stated by the VCH to

occur at Dovercourt and Clacton-on-Sea, this coast-haunting species has since been noted only in the first-mentioned locality— on 24 June 1933 (HEC).

*Leucania comma* L. (Shoulder-striped Wainscot)
Widely distributed and fairly common in a number of localities.

*Leucania unipuncta* Haw. (White-speck Wainscot)
This species, sometimes called the American Wainscot, has been recorded as follows: Bradwell-on-Sea, 7 October 1957, between 17 September and 1 October 1966 (3), 3 December 1970, 5 November 1971 and 4 November 1972 (2) (AJD); Westcliff-on-Sea, 20–21 July 1974 (HCH).

*Leucania l-album* L. (L-album Wainscot)
The only examples of this species, known also as the White L Wainscot, to have been noted in Essex were taken at Bradwell-on-Sea on 6 and 8 October 1972 (AJD).

*Leucania vitellina* Hübn. (Delicate Wainscot)
This rare immigrant from southern Europe has occurred in Essex on quite a few occasions. The VCH mentions only one, at Navestock near Brentwood in September 1900, but it has since been noted, singly, at the Sunk Light Vessel off Harwich on 26 September 1938 (W. P. Seabrook coll.); Westcliff-on-Sea *c.* 1939 and *c.* 1948 (HCH); Bradwell-on-Sea in 1949 (2), 1950 (11), 1951, 1954 (2), 1955, 1959 and 1962 (5) (AJD); and at Mucking on 9 September 1967 (RT).

*Leucania albipuncta* Schiff. (White-point Wainscot)
For some years this immigrant visited the county almost annually. The majority occurred at Bradwell-on-Sea, where it was recorded in 13 years between 1948 and 1963 inclusive with 27 in 1949, 58 in 1950 and 44 in 1951, numbers otherwise ranging from 2–19 (AJD). One or two appeared in south-east Essex (Westcliff-on-Sea, Hockley, Canewdon) in most years during this period (HCH, DM) and one was taken at Colne Point N.R. in August 1960 (JF). There are no records from the interior of the county.

*Leucania lythargyria* Esp. (Clay)
Generally distributed and common as it has always been.

*Leucania conigera* Schiff. (Brown-line Wainscot)
Also known as the Brown-line Bright-eye, this species is generally distributed in varying numbers and is quite common in some districts.

*Mythimna turca* L. (Double-line)
Very rare. Recorded in the VCH from Epping Forest and Brentwood and in 1907 as having been bred from ova obtained in the latter locality (*Entomologist*, 40:300). Sadly there is only one subsequent Essex record of this fine species—a single specimen at Stondon Massey on 20 July 1965 (DCT).

*Rhizedra lutosa* Hübn. (Large Wainscot)
Local. The VCH stated that this fine wainscot was widely distri-'

buted among reeds and was not uncommon in some coastal localities. It is still widespread in coastal and estuarine reed-beds from the Stour estuary round to Thames-side, along which it penetrates well into the Metropolis. In the interior it is found among reeds in the Chelmer Valley N.R., Little Baddow (GAP), and odd individuals have occurred in recent years at Collier Row, Romford (RRC), Thorndon Park/Ingrave (PFC, KWG), Coxtie Green (PJW), Stondon Massey (DCT), Takeley (GHBS) and Danbury Ridge (GAP).

*Arenostola pygmina* Haw. (Small Wainscot)

Local. The VCH recorded this diminutive wainscot from swampy meadows in the Colchester and Southend areas and the literature also mentions old records from Epping Forest, Maldon and Stansted. In recent years it has occurred sparingly around the coast and estuaries at Dovercourt (MEA), The Naze (GAP), Bradwell (AJD), Canewdon (HCH) and on the Thames estuary at Leigh-on-Sea (RRC), Thundersley (DGD), Pitsea (HCH), Thames-side (RT) and in east London at Plaistow (WLC); and inland at Thorndon Park/Ingrave (PCF, KWG), in the Chelmer Valley N.R., Little Baddow, and in damp woodland on Danbury Ridge (GAP), at Wickham Bishops (GCD), at North Ockendon, Stondon Massey and Ongar (DCT), and in Hatfield Forest and at Takeley (GHBS).

*Arenostola phragmitides* Hübn. (Fen Wainscot)

Local. The VCH stated that it was of general occurrence among reeds and this may still be the case. Recent coastal/estuarine records are: Dovercourt/Hamford Water, small numbers (MEA, JBF); Bradwell, fairly common (AJD); Rochford Hundred, not uncommon locally (DGD, HCH); Benfleet, 1934 (*Proc. S. Lond. ent. nat. Hist. Soc.*, 1933–4:24); Thames-side, not uncommon (RT). Inland it has been recorded sparingly in the Chelmer Valley N.R., Little Baddow (GAP), and at Ongar in 1964 (DCT), at Ingrave in 1969 (KWG) and on Danbury Ridge in 1974 (GAP).

*Nonagria sparganii* Esp. (Webb's Wainscot)

Local. This variable species, which was first recorded in England in 1879, seems to have reached Essex *c.* 1947 when it was first noted at Rochford and Leigh-on-Sea where it still occurs sparingly (HCH). To the west it is now found very locally at Thundersley (DGD) and has established itself on Thames-side west to E. Tilbury (RT). At Bradwell-on-Sea it occurred annually up to 1962 but has since been irregular (AJD). It was discovered at Rowhedge gravel-pits in 1956 (PB) and is now widespread there and present in other pits containing *Typha* (Reed-mace) at Fingringhoe and Thorington (JF). One was noted at the Naze N.R. in August 1972 (GAP, JKW). The only inland record to date concerns a colony which has established itself near Brentwood (PCF, KWG).

*Nonagria typhae* Thunb. (Bulrush Wainscot)
Fairly widespread. The VCH stated that this large species was to be found generally among *Typha* (Reed-mace) and this is no doubt still the case as it has been recorded in a number of coastal/estuarine and several inland localities in late years, albeit mostly at low density. From time to time it wanders to places some distance from the nearest food-plant. The fact that there are no recent records from the west side of the county is probably due to the paucity of recorders in this area. Occasional melanic specimens have recently occurred at Bradwell-on-Sea (AJD).

*Nonagria geminipunctata* Haw. (Twin-spot Wainscot)
Local. The VCH recorded this species from Alresford, Harwich, Mucking and Witham and there are also old records from Benfleet, Tilbury and Woodford. Today it is found locally on the coast and estuaries at Rochford (DGD, HCH), Bradwell-on-Sea (AJD) and at St. Osyth, Rowhedge and West Mersea (JF), while one occurred at Dovercourt in July 1969 (MEA) and another at Hamford Water in 1973 (JBF), and there are a series of records from Benfleet during the 1930s (e.g. *Proc. S. Lond. ent. nat. Hist. Soc.,* 1933–4:24) and another in 1973 (DGD). Inland one was recorded on Danbury Ridge in August 1971 (DGD) and another in the Chelmer Valley N.R., Little Baddow, on 29 August 1974 (GAP). It may prove to be more widespread in marshy localities than records suggest.

*Nonagria dissoluta* Treits. (Brown-veined Wainscot)
Decidedly local. The VCH does not record it but it was taken at Mucking in 1900 by CRNB, a number were found in the Harwich area in 1911 (*Entomologist*, 45:204) and there is an undated record from Tilbury (*London Nat.*, 35:34). Apart from one at Hamford Water in 1973 (JBF) it has been reported subsequently only from the southern half of the county. On or near the coast and estuaries it has occurred at Bradwell-on-Sea in nine years since 1949 (AJD); is not uncommon locally at Rochford, where one noted locality has been destroyed (DGD, HCH), and Leigh-on-Sea (HCH); and is regular in small to moderate numbers on Thames-side (RT). Inland it has occurred, singly, at Ingrave on 30 July 1967 (KWG), in Thorndon Park on 4 August 1973 (PCF), and in the Chelmer Valley N.R., Little Baddow, on 23 August 1971 (DGD, GAP) and 29 August 1974 (GAP). The dark form *dissoluta* Treits. is frequently taken.

*Coenobia rufa* Haw. (Small Rufous)
Extremely local. The VCH stated that this small species occurred at Harwich, Epping and Hainault and there are other old records from Wanstead Flats and Woodford. Odd specimens have occurred at Bradwell-on-Sea in five years since 1946 (AJD) but otherwise it has occurred only on Danbury Ridge where a small colony was dis-

covered in 1971 (DGD) and in Thorndon Park (2) in July 1974 (WLC).

*Chilodes maritima* Trausch. (Silky Wainscot)

Very local. The VCH gave Leigh-on-Sea, Alresford and Mucking as localities and other old ones are Harwich, Benfleet, Tilbury and Woodford. More recently, however, it has been found only at Bradwell-on-Sea where it is almost annual and fairly common in some years (AJD); in the Rochford Hundred where it is not un-common in reed-beds in five localities, abs. *wismariensis* Schmidt, *bipunctata* Haw. and *nigristriata* Staud. having all been recorded (HCH); on Thames-side where it is irregular and scarce (RT); and at Hamford Water on 26 July 1973 (JBF).

*Meristes trigrammica* Hufn. (Treble-lines)

Widespread. The VCH stated that this neatly-lined and variable species 'swarmed' at sugar, but although still widely distributed it does not approach abundance anywhere today and in some districts can only be described as scarce.

*Caradrina morpheus* Hufn. (Mottled Rustic)

This soberly-coloured species is common everywhere and abounds in favoured localities in some years.

*Caradrina alsines* Brahm (Uncertain)

Generally distributed and common in many districts.

*Caradrina blanda* Schiff. (Smooth Rustic)

More glossy than the last species, which it closely resembles, *C. blanda* is also generally distributed and common, or fairly so, over much of the county.

*Caradrina ambigua* Schiff. (Vine's Rustic)

Local; increasing and extending its range. Of a greyer tint than the three preceding members of the genus *Caradrina*, with conspicu-ous stigmata and white hind-wings, this moth was virtually confined to the south and south-west coasts until the 1940s when it began to extend its range into the home counties. It was first recorded in Essex at Canewdon in June 1934 (HCH) and is now widespread and locally common in the Rochford Hundred (DGD, HCH) and along Thames-side to Plaistow in east London (WLC). It is also common (although currently showing signs of a decline) at Bradwell-on-Sea where it first appeared in 1948 (AJD), and occurred at Walton-on-the-Naze in August 1971 (GAP, JKW) and Dovercourt in September 1974 (MEA). Inland it has so far been reported from Stondon Massey (DCT) and Thorndon Park (WLC), Danbury Ridge where it is slowly increasing (GAP), and Coxtie Green on 28 October 1972 (PJW).

*Caradrina clavipalpis* Scop. (Pale Mottled Willow)

Widespread and common, or fairly so, in most districts. However, it seems to be scarce towards the north-west of the county—one at Wimbish in 1962 (AME) is the only record—but this may be due to lack of coverage.

71

*Laphygma exigua* Hübn. (Small Mottled Willow)
This small species with pearly-white hind-wings is a well-known immigrant of quite frequent appearance which periodically arrives in fair numbers. It has been recorded most often in south-east Essex (DGD, HCH); at Bradwell-on-Sea where it has occurred in 13 years since 1947 with a maximum of 53 in 1962 but otherwise up to 11 (AJD); and in north-east Essex at Lexden, West Bergholt, Great Bromley and Colne Point N.R. (JF) and at Hamford Water (JBF). It is usually rare or absent well inland but one occurred at Buckhurst Hill in 1952 (*London Nat.*, 35:41), eight at Ongar in July 1962 (DCT), and three there (DCT) and single specimens at Hookend (RRC) and on Danbury Ridge (FBM, GAP) in autumn 1969. An exceptionally early record concerns one at Bradwell-on-Sea on 4 March 1952 (AJD).

*Dypterygia scabriuscula* L. (Bird's-wing)
Widespread. The VCH stated that this distinctive species was generally distributed and came freely to sugar, but today, although it is still present in most districts, it is far from common over much of its range. Preferring well-timbered localities it is often fairly common in such areas as the Colchester district (JF) and Danbury Ridge (GAP) but it is scarce in south-east Essex (DGD, HCH) while it has not been recorded in west or north-west Essex in recent years, though it was described by PBMA prior to 1950 as widespread but never common.

[*Prodenia litura* Fabr. (Mediterranean Brocade)
Larvae of this tropical and sub-tropical species were found on imported chrysanthemum in greenhouses at Nazeing in August 1964 (*Proc. Brit. ent. nat. Hist. Soc.*, 1(2):61).]

*Apamea lithoxylaea* Schiff. (Light Arches)
Generally distributed and common in many districts.

*Apamea monoglypha* Hufn. (Dark Arches)
Common everywhere.

*Apamea epomidion* Haw. (Clouded Brindle)
Local. The VCH recorded this species as rather scarce and local and much the same can be said of it today: if anything it is even less in evidence than formerly. Reported in recent years from some 18 localities scattered throughout the county, it is nowhere numerous and is distinctly scarce in most of its known haunts.

*Apamea crenata* Hufn. (Cloud-bordered Brindle)
Local. The VCH referred to this noctuid as generally distributed and usually common, but at the present time it seems to be even more local than *A. epomidion* (above) and equally scarce over much of its range. Its stronghold appears to be the well-timbered area between Ongar and the woodland south of Brentwood, within which it has lately been recorded, sometimes in fair numbers, from several localities. It occurs sparingly at Hadleigh and

Westcliff-on-Sea (HCH) and on Danbury Ridge (GAP). The only recent record from north-east Essex is of one at Dovercourt in August 1964 (MEA) while in the west and north-west, where it may well have been missed in the past, it has been noted only at Takeley, in 1973, and in Hatfield Forest and at Widdington, in 1974 (GHBS). It is not recorded from the north-west or north. The distinctive, uniform red-brown ab. *alopecurus* Esp. occurs not infrequently.

*Apamea sordens* Hufn. (Rustic Shoulder-knot)
Generally distributed and common.

*Apamea unanimis* Hübn. (Small Clouded Brindle)
Local. According to the VCH this inhabitant of moist places was 'frequently found in the larval state beside rivers and ditches' but due no doubt to intensive drainage it is now decidedly local. It is common at Bradwell-on-Sea (AJD), common locally at Benfleet and Westcliff-on-Sea (HCH), and quite common in the Chelmer Valley at Little Baddow (GAP) and Broomfield/Little Waltham (DP). Otherwise it has been reported as occurring sparingly or occasionally in recent years in the Ongar area (DCT), Thorndon Park/Ingrave (PCF, KWG), Doddinghurst (JTS), Danbury Ridge (GAP), Writtle (Writtle Ag. Coll. coll.), Thames-side (RT), North Ockendon (DCT), Birch Park (FDB:CNHS, JF), Mayland (PCF), Debden (AME) and Takeley (GHBS).

*Apamea oblonga* Haw. (Crescent-striped)
Local: virtually confined to the coast and estuaries. The VCH stated that this noctuid was to be found in suitable localities all along the coast from the Stour estuary to Southend-on-Sea. Its status does not seem to have changed as in recent years it has been recorded, often in good numbers, from 17 coastal and estuarine localities between Manningtree and Tilbury, a few having been found in the latter locality in 1938 (*London Nat.*, 34:96). It has also appeared at Cranham near Hornchurch (WLC).

*Apamea infesta* Ochs. (Large Nutmeg)
Described by the VCH merely as 'occasionally common at sugar', this species is widespread and fairly common locally in the southern half of the county, but appears to be thinly distributed and generally scarce in the north.

*Apamea remissa* Hübn. (Dusky Brocade)
This noctuid is widely distributed at varying density. However, it appears to be somewhat local and scarce in the west of the county.

*Apamea scolopacina* Esp. (Slender Brindle)
Local and extremely scarce. The VCH referred only to records from Harwich and Colchester but it was formerly noted also in Epping Forest (*London Nat.*, 34:100). It has since been found at Hadleigh where 1–2 were noted annually from 1933–39 (HCH) and at very

low density on Danbury Ridge (GAP), while it has occurred at Bradwell-on-Sea in eight years between 1948 and 1971 inclusive (AJD). All other modern records refer to single specimens, viz.: Buckhurst Hill, 1951 (*London Nat.*, 34:100); Dovercourt, July 1964 (MEA); Ingrave, August 1965 (KWG); Thames-side (RT) and Hookend (RRC), July 1969; Hamford Water, July 1972 (JBF); Wrabness, August 1972 (MEA); Thorndon Park, July 1973 (PCF).

*Apamea secalis* L. (Common Rustic)

Very common everywhere; sometimes abundant in particularly favoured localities and exhibiting a considerable variety of colour forms.

*Apamea ophiogramma* Esp. (Double-lobed)

This distinctive species is local and scarce although there is some evidence that it may currently be extending its range. The VCH stated that it was restricted to the southern half of Essex and this is largely true today although it has recently been found in three localities in the north of the county, single specimens having been noted at Dovercourt in 1970 and 1972 (MEA) and two in Birch Park (FDB:CNHS, JF) and one at Lexden in July 1973 (JF). Further south it is now common at Bradwell-on-Sea where it first appeared in 1949 (AJD), and occurs very sparingly in the Rochford Hundred where it is found only in gardens feeding on ribbon-grass, the cultivated version of *Phalaris arundinacea* (HCH); Thames-side (RT); Cranham (WLC); Thorndon Park/Ingrave (PCF, KWG); and on Danbury Ridge (range extension, 1973) and in the Chelmer Valley N.R., Little Baddow (GAP). Single specimens were noted at Coxtie Green in 1973 (PJW) and, in the west, at Takeley on 11 July 1973 (GHBS). It may well appear in other areas where the food-plant grows.

*Apamea ypsilon* Schiff. (Dingy Shears)

Somewhat local. Even allowing for the possibility that this indistinctive species, also known as the Dismal Brindle, has been under-recorded, or to some extent overlooked, in recent years it seems to be markedly less in evidence now that at the turn of the century when the VCH described it as generally common. It is currently reported only from the Rochford Hundred where it is stated to be common (HCH), and, at varying density, from Bradwell-on-Sea (AJD), Thames-side (RT), West Horndon (PCF), Ingrave (KWG), Hookend (RRC), Danbury Ridge (GAP), Takeley (GHBS), Hamford Water (JBF, GAP) and Wickham Bishops (GCD). It was also noted in Ongar Park Woods in 1929 (*Entomologist*, 63:42) and at Manuden prior to 1949 (PBMA).

*Eremobia ochroleuca* Schiff. (Dusky Sallow)

Widely distributed, mainly at low density. This most attractive ochreous species, which flies by day as well as night, was stated by the VCH lately to have reappeared in the east and south-east of

Essex after an absence from the county of several years, prior to which it had been common and generally distributed. Today it is fairly widespread, the districts in which it is noted annually being too numerous to list. The coastal fringe is probably its stronghold as it is found in all suitable localities from Dovercourt round to Thames-side, but it is also well represented in the Brentwood area (KWG *et al.*) and is fairly common in some years on Danbury Ridge (GAP).

*Procus strigilis* Clerck (Marbled Minor)
Generally distributed and common. The melanic ab. *aethiops* Haw. is of frequent occurrence.

*Procus latruncula* Schiff. (Tawny Minor)
Separated from *P. strigilis* as recently as the 1930s this species is known to be widespread at varying density and may prove to be generally distributed as it is easily confused with examples of the last species. The melanic ab. *aeruginis* Edel. & Tams is prevalent.

*Procus versicolor* Borkh. (Rufous Minor)
Separated in 1932 and first recognised as British in 1937, this species has so far been identified in Essex on only one occasion— at Ashdon (3) in July 1971 (RJR).

*Procus fasciuncula* Haw. (Middle-barred Minor)
Generally distributed and common, or fairly so, in a number of areas.

*Procus literosa* Haw. (Rosy Minor)
Local. The VCH indicated that this coast-oriented, vinous-tinged minor was scarce and local and most prevalent on the 'south coast', i.e. the Thames estuary. With the reservation that it is no more numerous on Thames-side than in a number of other coastal and estuarine localities, its status remains the same today. The only inland records are: Ingrave, several in 1967–68 (KWG); Ongar and Stondon Massey, occasionally (DCT); Wickham Bishops, 1969 (GCD); Gt. Horkesley, two in 1970 (FDB:CNHS); Birch Park, 28 July 1973 (FDB:CNHS, JF); Takeley, 1974 (GHBS).

*Procus furuncula* Schiff. (Cloaked Minor)
Generally distributed and common: especially well represented in some coastal localities where at times it has been described as abundant.

*Luperina testacea* Schiff. (Flounced Rustic)
Generally distributed and common, it is sometimes abundant on parts of the coast and estuaries.

*Euplexia lucipara* L. (Small Angle-shades)
Generally distributed and common, or fairly so, in many localities. However, it appears to be subject to periods of scarcity in some areas: formerly well-represented in west Essex it was described as only occasional in 1949 (*Trans. Bishop's Stortford nat. Hist. Soc.*, 1; *List of Lepidoptera*: 29) and has seldom been noted there since,

although the paucity of records may be due to under-recording; while it was not recorded from Bradwell-on-Sea, where it is now common, between 1945 and 1954 (AJD).

*Phlogophora meticulosa* L. (Angle-shades)
This well-known and distinctive species is common and universally distributed. Two examples of the rare and beautiful red ab. *roseobrunnea* Warren were taken at Westcliff-on-Sea on 6 September 1951 and 11 August 1960 (HCH).

*Thalpophila matura* Hufn. (Straw Underwing)
This attractive species is generally distributed and is fairly common in some districts, although perhaps nowhere really numerous. It is stated to have become less common in west Essex by 1949 (*Trans. Bishop's Stortford nat. Hist. Soc.,* 1; *List of Lepidoptera*: 29) and to have decreased in the last decade around Colchester (JF) but there is no evidence of a general decline.

*Petilampa minima* Haw. (Small Dotted Buff)
This moth of damp situations appears to be widely distributed and locally common over much of the county but does not seem to have been recorded in recent years anywhere in east Essex, except at Bradwell-on-Sea, where it is of almost annual occurrence but rather scarce (AJD), and at Hamford Water in 1973 (JBF).

*Hapalotis venustula* Hübn. (Rosy Marbled)
This rather rare British species is confined to Essex and a few southern counties where it is extremely local but often common in its few restricted localities. The VCH stated that this tiny whitish moth with a delicate rosy tinge had occurred 'rather freely' in several parts of Epping Forest and at Warley near Brentwood but it seems to have disappeared from the first locality before the turn of the century, having last been recorded there in 1885 (*Entomologist,* 18:203). It has, however, persisted in the Brentwood area where it was last noted as recently as 1970 (RRC). Found abundantly on Danbury Ridge in 1929 (*Entomologist,* 62:211), it is still common locally in that locality (GAP). The only other records relate to stragglers at Bradwell-on-Sea in 1958 (2) and 1971 (AJD) and on Thames-side on 19 June and 14 July 1970 (RT).

*Celaena haworthii* Curt. (Haworth's Minor)
The only Essex record of this moor and fenland species, whose larvae feed on *Eriophorum vaginatum* (Cotton-grass) is of one at Bradwell-on-Sea on 1 August 1951 (AJD).

*Celaena leucostigma* Hübn. (The Crescent)
Local. The only locality mentioned by the VCH is Colchester, where apparently the population consisted of the attractive ab. *fibrosa* Hübn., but it was also taken at Stansted in 1875 (*Entomologist,* 8:281). Today it is known to occur on Thames-side where it is not uncommon locally, ab. *fibrosa* occurring occasionally (RT); in south-east Essex at Rochford and Leigh-on-Sea (HCH) and at

Thundersley where it is scarce (DGD); at Bradwell-on-Sea where it is fairly common (AJD); and in the Chelmer Valley N.R., Little Baddow, where it is quite common, ab. *fibrosa* predominating (GAP). The only other records concern single specimens at Stondon Massey on 17 August 1964 (DCT), The Naze on 28 August 1972 (GAP, JKW), Birch Park on 28 July 1973 (FDB:CNHS, JF) and Hornchurch on 21 August 1973 (WLC).

*Hydraecia oculea* L. (Ear)
Widely distributed at low to medium density.

*Hydraecia paludis* Tutt (Saltern Ear)
Widespread on the coast. This moth was separated from *H. oculea* (above) early this century and consequently is not mentioned as such in the VCH, although the 'generally larger and paler' coast 'forms' of *oculea* to which it refers clearly relate to the present species. As its vernacular name suggests, *paludis* is confined to the saltings and their vicinity, and it is widespread, becoming fairly common in places, along the coast and estuaries from Dovercourt in the north-east round to the Thames estuary. Stragglers appear occasionally a short distance inland but the only record for the interior is of one at Ongar on 22 August 1966 (DCT).

*Gortyna micacea* Esp. (Rosy Rustic)
Generally distributed. Common in many areas and especially prevalent in marshy localities where it sometimes approaches abundance.

*Gortyna borelii* Pierret (Fisher's Estuarine)
First recorded in Essex in autumn 1968 (JBF; *Ent. Rec.*, 83:51 & 52 with photograph), this handsome species is now known to be established—as it may always have been—in one restricted locality, its only known British station, where all possible steps are being taken to protect it.

*Gortyna petasitis* Doubl. (Butterbur)
This quite large species, which is very local in southern England, has been recorded in Essex on only two occasions, both in 1959. Single specimens occurred at Bradwell-on-Sea on 6 August (AJD) and at Rowhedge in the same month (JF).

*Gortyna flavago* Schiff. (Frosted Orange)
Generally distributed; perhaps nowhere really numerous but fairly common in a number of districts.

*Dicycla oo* L. (Heart)
Very local and scarce. The VCH stated that this attractive species was sometimes to be found freely in many places in south Essex but rarely in the north. It occurs regularly at low density at Ongar and Stondon Massey (DCT); and other post-VCH records, all from the southern half of the county, are: Brentwood, larva, 11 May 1946 (*Proc. S. Lond. ent. nat. Hist. Soc.*, 1946–7:70); Epping, bred from a larva, 1947 (*Essex Nat.*, 28:79); Farnham, nr. Bishop's

Stortford, larvae, 1948 (PBMA); Bradwell-on-Sea, 12 July 1955 (AJD); Hockley, several, 1954–57 (*Essex Nat.*, 29:261; 30:69 & 122); Westcliff-on-Sea, 1955 (HCH).

*Cosmia pyralina* Schiff. (Lunar-spotted Pinion)
Widely if not generally distributed and fairly numerous in a number of districts. The VCH stated that it was rare and local and mentioned only five localities for it: thus it seems to be one of the few Essex species to have increased this century.

*Cosmia affinis* L. (Lesser-spotted Pinion)
Widespread. According to the VCH this species, which closely resembles *C. pyralina* (above) but has darker hind-wings and is slightly smaller, was widely distributed at the turn of the century and was not uncommon in some 'elm districts'. The same can be said of it today: while it is not quite as widespread as *pyralina* it is nevertheless fairly well distributed and is common in some areas, notably the Rochford Hundred (DGD, HCH). It appears to be very scarce, or is perhaps under-recorded, in the west and north-west.

*Cosmia diffinis* L. (White-spotted Pinion)
Local. The VCH stated that this species was as widespread as *C. affinis* (above) but it is now decidedly local and apparently common only in parts of south-east Essex (HCH). Otherwise it has been recorded in recent years from 14 localities scattered throughout the county, except the centre and mid-north.

*Cosmia trapezina* L. (Dun-bar)
Generally distributed and common, this extremely variable species is very numerous in some well-timbered districts.

*Enargia paleacea* Esp. (Angle-striped Sallow)
Apart from three late 19th century records the only occurrences of this fine species, which in the southern half of England is regarded as a rare immigrant, are of single specimens at Bradwell-on-Sea on 14 August 1964 (AJD), Rayleigh on 20 August 1964 (DM), and Danbury Ridge on 6 August 1970 and 23 July 1972 (GAP).

*Zenobia retusa* L. (Double Kidney)
Very rare, possibly extinct. The VCH gave it as scarce and local and mentioned Epping, Harwich, Layer Marney and Rainham as localities. There is only one later record—of three bred from larvae found at Benfleet in 1936 (HCH).

*Zenobia subtusa* Schiff. (Olive)
Local. The VCH indicated that it had formerly been frequent among poplars but had become less common. At the present time it is known to occur in comparatively few localities. It is generally distributed at low density in south-east Essex (DGD, HCH) and is fairly common at Bradwell-on-Sea (AJD) and on Danbury Ridge (GAP). In the Brentwood area it occurs at Ingrave (KWG) and was noted at Doddinghurst in 1970 (JTS), Hookend in 1971 (RRC) and Coxtie Green in 1974 (PJW). It has also been found recently at

North Ockendon and near Ongar (DCT) and at Ashdon (RJR).

*Panemeria tenebrata* Scop. (Small Yellow Underwing)

Local. According to the VCH this attractive little day-flier was once frequently to be seen in flowery spaces, but due to habitat destruction, spraying and other adverse factors it has become decidedly local. It is found sparsely in the Rochford Hundred (HCH), is uncommon at Bradwell-on-Sea (AJD) and is still fairly common locally on Danbury Ridge (GAP). The only other recent records concern single specimens on Shenfield Common on 1 June 1942 (EFW), in Hatfield Forest on 6 June 1955 (GHBS), at Chigwell Row in May 1973 (IS), and at Dunton and near Basildon in June 1973 (RT), but because of its diminutive size it may have been overlooked in other still suitable localities.

*Amphipyra pyramidea* L. (Copper Underwing)

Generally distributed and common in many areas.

*Amphipyra berbera* Rungs. (Drab Copper Underwing)

This species has only recently been separated from *A. pyramidea* (above) and thus resembles it very closely: apart from the greater contrast which *pyramidea* exhibits in the vertical striping on the sides of the thorax, the marginal differences are mostly to be found on the undersides of the hind-wings. It follows that the distribution of the present species in Essex, as elsewhere, has yet to be worked out. Observations to date suggest that the first *berbera* emerge (in late July) a few days earlier than *pyramidea*. The earliest known Essex record is of two at Chelmsford in 1938 (W. P. Seabrook coll.). On Danbury Ridge it appears to be nearly as common as *pyramidea* (GAP) while in the Brentwood area all specimens in a series of six '*pyramidea*' from Ingrave proved to be the present species (KWG) and it has also been noted at Hookend (RRC). At Dovercourt *berbera* appears to be well represented in some years (MEA). It has also been reported from Benfleet (DGD), Bradwell-on-Sea (AJD) and Wickham Bishops (GCD).

*Amphipyra tragopoginis* Clerck (Mouse)

Common or very common everywhere.

*Rusina tenebrosa* Hübn. (Brown Rustic)

Generally distributed and common. Two dilute specimens occurred at Thorndon Park in 1973 (PCF).

*Mormo maura* L. (Old Lady)

Widespread, declining. The VCH described this large, sombre species as generally common. But although it is still widely, perhaps even universally, distributed it has become very scarce in Essex as in other counties. Its much reduced numbers have been apparent for at least a decade, but there is some evidence that the decline set in in the early 1950s. The only locality from which it has been reported in numbers in recent years is Dovercourt, where, e.g., a total of 32 came to light in 1968 (MEA).

79

*Cryphia perla* Schiff. (Marbled Beauty)

Described in the VCH as common, this attractive little noctuid, though still generally distributed, is rather scarce in many districts today and numerous in few. The melanic ab. *suffusa* Tutt is scarce but regular, constituting about 5 per cent of all examples in the Southend-on-Sea area; 1–2 examples of ab. *flavescens* Tutt, which has an orange ground colour, appear at Westcliff-on-Sea annually; and one of only three known examples of ab. *aureolichenea* Cockayne was taken at Westcliff-on-Sea on 11 August 1951 (HCH).

*Moma alpium* Osbeck (Scarce Merveille-du-Jour)

Very rare; probably extinct. Stated in the VCH to occur 'north of Colchester', this beautiful moth has otherwise been recorded (by HCH) only at Belfairs, Hadleigh (1), in June 1935 and at Rettendon (in a wood which was clear-felled and replanted during the 1939–45 war) in June 1935 (1) and June 1936 (2).

*Apatele leporina* L. (Miller)

Fairly widespread; not common. The VCH described this attractive greyish-white species as far from common and mentioned only three localities. It is still generally scarce, and in some places of only irregular occurrence, but it is known to enjoy a fairly wide distribution, having been recorded in 16 widely scattered localities in recent years. It is nowhere numerous and has been described as fairly common only on Danbury Ridge (GAP).

*Apatele aceris* L. (Sycamore Dagger)

Widespread. The VCH stated that it occurred in several localities but had disappeared from the Colchester district: however, it is currently quite common at Lexden (JF). Generally by no means numerous and decidedly scarce in some areas it is nevertheless more widely distributed than the last species. The blackish ab. *candelisequa* Esp. is not infrequent in the Rochford Hundred (HCH).

*Apatele megacephala* Schiff. (Poplar Dagger)

Widely, perhaps generally, distributed and common in a number of districts.

*Apatele alni* L. (Alder Dagger)

Local and scarce. This handsome black, grey and white moth is one of those species which the use of the mercury vapour lamp has shown to be markedly less rare than had previously been supposed. The VCH described it as very rare, giving only Colchester and Wormingford as localities, and there are no further records until 1958–62 when 1–2 occurred annually in the Colchester area at Lexden, Old Heath and Berechurch (JF). All subsequent records are given: Ongar, June 1963 (DCT); Loughton, larva, August 1964 (P. W. Glassborrow *per* EFW); Romford, June 1967 (RRC); Danbury Ridge, 1–2 most years since 1968 (GAP); Bradwell, singly in 1968, 1969 and 1970 (AJD); Doddinghurst (JTS) and Hookend (RRC), June 1970; Hamford Water, June 1970 and May 1971

The shingle ridge and shore vegetational zones at Colne Point Nature Reserve, haunt of a number of specialised moth species. Photo: K. Huggett

The Essex salt-marshes provide an important and specialised habitat for moths. These saltings at the Strood, West Mersea, are the haunt of *Malacosoma castrensis* L. (Ground Lackey), *Leucania favicolor* Barr. (Mathew's Wainscot), *Scopula*

(JBF); Stondon Massey, May 1971 (DCT); Navestock Side, larva, July 1971 (Mrs. D. M. Williams *per* EFW); Ingrave, June 1973 (KWG).

*Apatele tridens* Schiff. (Dark Dagger)

The near-impossibility of distinguishing this moth from the next, except by examination of the genitalia or in the larval stage, makes any assessment of its status difficult. The VCH regarded it as the scarcer of the two species, though of general occurrence: such present-day evidence as we have certainly suggests that it is generally far from common but that it may still be widely distributed.

*Apatele psi* L. (Grey Dagger)

Generally distributed and common; the conspicuous larva is a familiar sight.

*Apatele rumicis* L. (Knot-grass)

Generally distributed and common in many districts, the black ab. *salicis* Curt. being prevalent.

*Craniophora ligustri* Schiff. (Coronet)

Very rare. Although formerly recorded as scarce at Alresford and Colchester (VCH) and at Maldon (*Essex Field Club Trans.*, 3:44), the only modern record of this moth, alternatively known as the Crown, is of one on Danbury Ridge on 24 July 1969 (GAP).

*Simyra venosa* Borkh. (Powdered Dagger)

Very local; unknown before 1949. This species, which is also known as the Powdered Wainscot or the Reed Dagger, has been recorded in only four Essex localities, all on or near the coast. It has appeared at Bradwell-on-Sea in 13 years between 1949 and 1972 inclusive (AJD); small colonies were found at Rowhedge and Alresford gravel-pits on either side of the Colne estuary in 1957 and 1958 (JF); and one was taken at Hamford Water in 1969 or 1970 (JBF).

*Cucullia umbratica* L. (Shark)

Generally distributed at varying density: seemingly most numerous on the east side of the county.

*Cucullia asteris* Schiff. (Starwort)

Virtually confined to the coast and its vicinity. The VCH gave only Dovercourt, Southend and Benfleet as localities for this shark, the beautifully marked larva of which feeds on *Aster tripolium* (Sea-aster) and occasionally on garden varieties of the genus, but it is now known to be widespread round the coast and estuaries from Manningtree to Stanford-le-Hope, and is common in a number of places. Single specimens at Ingrave on 14 and 28 June 1969 (KWG) are the only inland records.

*Cucullia chamomillae* Schiff. (Chamomile Shark)

Widespread, as stated in the VCH, but scarce in most districts, particularly in the west, apparently occurring at fairly high density only in the south-east from the Blackwater estuary southwards.

*Cucullia absinthii* L. (Pale Wormwood Shark)

Rather rare: unknown before 1949 and noted only in the south-east and south. All records are given: Newbury Park, Ilford, 22 June 1949 (*Essex Nat.*, 28:211); Hockley, singly in 1956 and 1957 (*Essex Nat.*, 30:69, 122 & 208); Westcliff-on-Sea, 12 August 1958 (*Essex Nat.*, 30:208); Bradwell-on-Sea, 31 July 1962 (AJD); Thames-side, occasional specimens from 1965 onwards (RT); seven larvae, September 1973 (DGD); Grays (2), July 1973 (DGD).

*Cucullia artemisiae* Hufn. (Scarce Wormwood Shark)

The only Essex record of this exceedingly rare British species is of a larva obtained at Nazeing on the western border of the county on 4 September 1971; the imago emerged on 2 July 1972 (JR).

*Cucullia verbasci* L. (Mullein Shark)

Fairly widely distributed. Described in the VCH as common in the larval state, this shark is far less in evidence today, although it seems still to be fairly widespread as in recent years it has been recorded intermittently, mostly as larvae, from 19 localities scattered throughout the county, except the east and south-west.

*Cucullia lychnitis* Ramb. (Striped Lychnis)

The only Essex record is of a single specimen at Bradwell-on-Sea on 3 June 1951 (AJD).

*Lithomoia solidaginis* Hübn. (Golden Rod Brindle)

This moth has occurred in Essex only in 1954 during a unique immigration of the German form *cinerascens* Staud. Single specimens then occurred at Westcliff-on-Sea on 26 August (HCH) and at Bradwell-on-Sea (AJD) and Hockley (DM) on 28 August.

*Lithophane semibrunnea* Haw. (Tawny Pinion)

Very local and scarce. Even less in evidence than when the VCH described it as scarce and local, this moth has been found regularly in recent years only at Lexden, Colchester (JF). It has occurred in eight years between 1951 and 1972 inclusive at Bradwell-on-Sea (AJD) but otherwise has been noted, singly, only at Chelmsford in 1935 (W. P. Seabrook coll.); in the north-east at Mistley on 9 October 1938 (HEC), Walton-on-the-Naze on 18 October 1969 (JKW), Wix on 26 October 1974 (RM) and Hamford Water in 1974 (JBF); and on Thames-side on 27 September 1970 (RT).

*Lithophane ornitopus* Hufn. (Grey Shoulder-knot)

Widespread. This attractive pale grey species which appears in the late autumn and again, after hibernation, in the spring, is widely distributed but seems to be scarce or fairly so in most districts. The VCH gives the impression that its status was much the same at the turn of the century.

*Xylena exsoleta* L. (Sword-grass)

Very local and scarce. The VCH considered this fine moth to be more common than the next. Today the reverse appears to be true but both are now in any case much rarer than the VCH seemed to suggest. The only post-1925 records of the present species are: Benfleet, singly in 1935, 1937 and 1938 (HCH); near Colchester (Old Heath, Lexden, West Bergholt), occasional (JF); Bradwell-on-Sea, 1957 and 1964 (AJD); Epping Forest, 1974 (NE).

*Xylena vetusta* Hübn. (Red Sword-grass)
Local and scarce. Although marginally less rare nowadays than the last species, *X. vetusta* is still very scarce. Post-1925 records are: Bradwell-on-Sea, odd specimens in most years (AJD); Benfleet, several in the late 1930s (HCH); near Colchester (Lexden and Donyland Woods), 1959 and 1960 (JF); Thundersley (DGD) and Coxtie Green (PJW), 1971; Ongar, 1972 (DCT).

*Xylocampa areola* Esp. (Early Grey)
Generally distributed and common. The dark blackish-brown ab. *nigrabrunnea* Huggins, first taken at Westcliff-on-Sea on 3 June 1955 (HCH), has been noted in south-east Essex on four occasions.

*Calophasia lunula* Hufn. (Toadflax Brocade)
Three specimens of this continental species were said to have been taken near Epping in June 1817 (*Entomologist*, 73:111). Otherwise the only Essex records concern an imago at Bradwell-on-Sea on 11 August 1951 (AJD) and three larvae on 19 September 1953 and one in 1954 at Wakering (HCH).

*Brachionycha sphinx* Hufn. (Sprawler)
Rather local. This attractive black-streaked, pale grey-brown moth of the late autumn was described by the VCH as 'very generally distributed but not common'. Today it seems to be somewhat local as it has been reported in recent years from only 15 scattered localities. Half of these are on the east side of the county north to Colchester and none is to the south or south-west of Brentwood, except for Thorndon Park (PCF). It is generally scarce where it does occur and is noted as fairly common only on Danbury Ridge (GAP) and at Bradwell-on-Sea (AJD).

*Bombycia viminalis* F. (Minor Shoulder-knot)
Local. The VCH stated that this small noctuid could be taken freely in the larval state but today it is decidedly local and for the most part scarce. It has been noted in recent years at Hamford Water (JBF), Bradwell-on-Sea (AJD), Westcliff-on-Sea (HCH), Lexden (JF), Warley (*Proc. S. Lond. ent. nat. Hist. Soc*, 1933–4: 15), Thorndon Park (PCF), Ongar (DCT), Quendon (AME), Hatfield Forest (GHBS) and Danbury Ridge (GAP), but is said to be fairly common only in the latter locality.

*Aporophyla lutulenta* Schiff. (Deep Brown Dart)
Local. The VCH described this species as scarce and local and much the same can still be said of it. Its Essex headquarters seem to be in the east and south-east as it is described as fairly common in the Rochford Hundred (HCH), on Thames-side (RT) and in some years on Danbury Ridge (GAP), and common at Bradwell-on-Sea

(AJD). Otherwise it has been recorded, singly or in small numbers, at Hamford Water (JBF), Dovercourt (MEA), Chelmsford (GAP), Coxtie Green (PJW), South Weald Park (RRC) and Thorndon Park/Ingrave (PCF, KWG). It is possible that the complete absence of records from the north and west may be due to the paucity of observers in those areas.

*Aporophyla lunula* Stroem (Black Rustic)
Very rare. The only Essex record of this species, which has recently become more prevalent in the southern counties, concerns a very small male at mercury vapour light at Westcliff-on-Sea on 21 September 1961 which may well have been an immigrant (HCH).

*Aporophyla australis* Boisd. (Feathered Brindle)
This coast sands species has been recorded only twice in Essex—at St. Osyth (larva) prior to 1903 (VCH) and Colne Point N.R. (imago) on 8 October 1969 (RAS *per* HCH).

*Allophyes oxyacanthae* L. (Green-brindled Crescent)
Generally distributed and common in a number of areas. The dark brown ab. *capucina* Mill. is much in evidence and predominates in some districts.

*Griposia aprilina* L. (Merveille-du-Jour)
Widespread. The VCH described this beautiful green autumnal moth as common and occurring throughout the county. It is still widely distributed, having been reported in recent years from some 19 localities, but it is scarce in many of these districts and even in extensive oak woodland it is usually far from numerous.

*Eumichtis adusta* Esp. (Dark Brocade)
Local and scarce. This appears to be another species which has decreased as, according to the VCH, it once occurred generally. It is regular in small numbers on Thames-side (RT), occurs sparingly in the Dovercourt/Hamford Water area (MEA, JBF), and has also been noted at Bradwell-on-Sea (AJD), Danbury Ridge (GAP), Alder Carr N.R., Little Waltham (DP), Thorndon Park/Ingrave (PCF, KWG) and Kingsford Bridge Marsh N.R., Layer-de-la-Haye (JF:CNHS). However, the fact that it has been reported in late years from Stansted, Ugley and Quendon (PBMA), Birchanger (CM), Hatfield Forest and Takeley (GHBS) and Ashdon (RJR), all in west or north-west Essex, suggests that it may be more widespread in that part of the county than elsewhere.

*Eumichtis lichenea* Hübn. (Feathered Ranunculus)
Very local. Not recorded in the VCH, this coastal species is found at Bradwell-on-Sea (AJD) and Hamford Water (JBF), in both of which localities it is stated to be fairly common, while one appeared at Dovercourt in October 1973 (MEA) and *c.* 10 at Walton-on-the-Naze in late September 1974 (JKW). Two examples which occurred inland in 1972 at Coxtie Green on 5 October (PJW) and

on Danbury Ridge on 13 October (GAP) may possibly have been immigrants.

*Parastichtis suspecta* Hübn. (Suspected)
Local. The VCH stated that this smallish noctuid was very local, mentioning only Brentwood and Rainham as localities. There is also an old, undated record from Epping Forest in the *London Naturalist* (35:51) while, within our period, it was described as abundant in Ongar Park Wood in July 1929 (*Entomologist*, 63:41). More recently it has been reported only from Danbury Ridge where it is fairly common in some years (GAP), Bradwell-on-Sea where it is uncommon and irregular, having occurred in 10 years between 1956 and 1972 inclusive (AJD), and Ingrave on 21 July 1971 (KWG).

*Dryobotodes eremita* F. (Brindled Green)
Widely distributed. The VCH described this attractive greenish species as of general occurrence and it is still widespread in varying numbers today, probably being found wherever oak is well represented.

*Antitype flavicincta* Schiff. (Large Ranunculus)
Local and scarce. The VCH failed to record it, yet there are several old records in the literature—from Epping, Leyton, Chingford, Maldon and Stansted Mountfitchet. In the south it is regular in small numbers at Stanford-le-Hope (RT) and was taken in 1951 and 1953 at Grays and in 1952–53 at Horndon-on-the-Hill (T. G. Pearman coll.). In the Chelmsford area several were taken at Great Baddow in 1936–37 (W. P. Seabrook coll.), one in the town in 1951 (GAP) and four at Writtle in 1967 (Writtle Ag. Coll. coll.). In and around Colchester it occurred regularly at Lexden from 1958–61 and in 1974 (JF) and was noted in the town in 1963 (*Essex Nat.*, 31:109) and at Aldham (3) in 1971 (MRSM). Further to the north-east it is recorded from Mistley and Lawford (ICR) and occurred at Walton-on-the-Naze in 1974 (JKW). The only other records are of single examples at Bradwell-on-Sea in 1949 (AJD), Thundersley in 1963 (DGD), Ingrave in 1966 (KWG) and Tiptree in 1967 (FDB). There are no modern records for the western half of the county.

*Eupsilia transversa* Hufn. (Satellite)
Widespread. This attractive noctuid, which flies in the autumn and spring and on some warm winter nights, was described by the VCH as common throughout the county. It is still widely, perhaps generally, distributed and is fairly common in some districts.

*Omphaloscelis lunosa* Haw. (Lunar Underwing)
This well-marked species is widely distributed and well established in a number of districts although it is given to considerable fluctuation in numbers.

*Agrochola lota* Clerck (Red-Line Quaker)
Widely distributed at varying density.

*Agrochola macilenta* Hübn. (Yellow-line Quaker)
Fairly widespread. The VCH described this species, like the last, as generally common, but at the present time the insect does not appear to be as widely distributed as *A. lota*, although it is found in a number of localities and is common in some. The complete absence of records during the past half-century from the west or north-west may be due to the paucity of recorders.

*Agrochola circellaris* Hufn. (Brick)
Generally distributed and numerous in a number of districts.

*Agrochola lychnidis* Schiff. (Beaded Chestnut)
Common everywhere.

*Anchoscelis helvola* L. (Flounced Chestnut)
Fairly widespread. Another autumnal species described by the VCH as generally common, this attractive insect seems to be somewhat local today. Noted in recent years in some 14 widespread localities it is common or fairly so in some but scarce in others. As with *A. macilenta* (above) there are no recent records from west Essex.

*Anchoscelis litura* L. (Brown-spot Pinion)
Generally distributed at widely varying density.

*Atethmia xerampelina* Esp. (Centre-barred Sallow)
Widely distributed. The VCH stated that this attractive ash-feeder was apparently scarce and local and gave only four localities for it. Today it is known to be fairly widespread: noted in some 16 localities in recent years it is quite common in a number of districts. In north-east Essex, however, it is recorded only from Mistley (ICR).

*Tiliacea citrago* L. (Orange Sallow)
Widely distributed; not common. The statement in the VCH that this colourful autumnal moth was well distributed among lime holds good today, as it has been reported during the past half-century from 17 localities though in none can it be described as common: on the contrary it is mostly scarce and in some areas of irregular occurrence. Its stronghold appears to be in the Colchester area as it has appeared in six localities in and around the town (JF *et al.*): otherwise it is scattered throughout the county except that the only recent record from the west or north-west is of one at Saffron Walden in 1968 (AME).

*Tiliacea aurago* Schiff. (Barred Sallow)
Widespread. According to the VCH this 'sallow' was very scarce at the turn of the century in north Essex but more frequent in the south. Today it is known to be widespread: recorded from 20 localities in recent years, it occurs at low density over much of its range but is fairly common in several districts.

*Citria lutea* Stroem (Pink-barred Sallow)
Widespread. Stated by the VCH to be quite common generally

this species is still widespread, though rather less so than *T. aurago*. Its range and density are not dissimilar from those of the last species but it is numerous in rather more localities although apparently scarcer than *T. aurago* in a few.

*Cirrhia icteritia* Hufn. (Common Sallow)
Widely distributed and common in a number of districts.

*Cirrhia gilvago* Schiff. (Dusky-lemon Sallow)
Fairly widespread; not common. The VCH inferred that this dusky species was widely distributed and quite common in good seasons: if this was the case it is much less in evidence today as it has been recorded of late in only 14 widely scattered localities, the majority in the southern half of the county. In most of them it is very scarce. Its stronghold appears to be the Dengie and Rochford Hundreds in the east and south-east: there it is reported to be fairly common at Bradwell-on-Sea (AJD), Hullbridge and West-cliff-on-Sea (HCH) and at Thundersley (DGD).

*Cirrhia ocellaris* Borkh. (Pale-lemon Sallow)
Very local and scarce. The VCH cited only two records—from Feering, near Kelvedon, and Southend-on-Sea—while one was taken at Mucking in September 1901 (CRNB). The Colchester district is its present-day stronghold: there it was noted at Lexden in September 1959 (2) and September 1961 (2) (JF), Old Heath in October 1960 (JF) and Cannock Mill in October 1969 (FDB: CNHS). The only other records are of two at Leigh-on-Sea in 1934 (HCH), single specimens at Bradwell-on-Sea in 1956, 1957 and 1961 (AJD) and two at Plaistow (east London) in September 1971 (WLC).

*Conistra vaccinii* L. (Common Chestnut)
Generally distributed and mostly common, extremely so in some oak woodlands; still frequent in the spring after hibernation.

*Conistra ligula* Esp. (Dark Chestnut)
Widespread. The VCH found this species to be much scarcer than the last and this is still the case: while probably of general distribution it occurs at quite low density over much of the county and is doubtfully numerous anywhere.

*Bena prasinana* L. (Green Silver-lines)
This attractive green moth is to be found in all well-timbered districts and is common in some years in the more extensively wooded areas.

*Pseudoips bicolorana* Fuessl. (Scarce Silver-lines)
Widespread. This equally attractive species was described by the VCH as far from common but widely distributed in parks and woods. Today it seems to be found wherever oak occurs and although its density is low over much of its range it is quite common in some districts, notably in the Rochford Hundred (HCH) and on Danbury Ridge, where it outnumbers *B. prasinana* in most

years (GAP). At Ongar and Stondon Massey there is evidence of a recent increase (DCT). One was seen a few years ago as near to Inner London as Newham (B. Betts *per* DCT).

*Earias clorana* L. (Cream-bordered Green)
Very local and scarce. The VCH stated that this small green and white moth was sometimes common among osiers but due no doubt to the extensive drainage of marshes it is seldom encountered today. The only recent records, all from the southern estuary areas, are: Bradwell-on-Sea, regular up to 1961 but none since (AJD); Canvey Island, larva, 2 September 1951 (*Proc. S. Lond. ent. nat. Hist. Soc.*, 1951–2:78); Westcliff-on-Sea, 1955, 1957 and 1958 (HCH); Thames-side, 19 June and 4 July 1967 and 15 July 1969 (RT); Creeksea, 29 June 1971 (DGD).

*Nycteola revayana* Scop. (Large Marbled Tortrix)
Apparently local and mostly scarce, as it was said to be by the VCH, but possibly this highly variable, small tortrix-like moth, also known as the Oak nycteoline, has been overlooked in some districts, especially as the predominantly dingy brown colouration of most Essex specimens makes the insect inconspicuous. All recent records are given: Warley, larvae, June 1933 (*Proc. S. Lond. ent. nat. Hist. Soc.*, 1933–4:15); Mistley, October 1936 (HEC); Benfleet, pupa, July 1937 (*Proc. S. Lond. ent. nat. Hist. Soc.*, 1937–8:47); Hatfield Forest, prior to 1950 (PBMA); Debden, 1965 and 1967 (AME); Langdon Hills, May 1969 (RT); Hamford Water, two in 1970 (JBF); Rochford Hundred, not uncommon locally, all melanic (DGD, HCH); Bradwell-on-Sea, occurs almost annually in small numbers (AJD); Danbury Ridge, rather scarce (GAP).

*Lithacodia fasciana* L. (Marbled White-spot)
Local and scarce. This species appears to be less widespread than formerly as the VCH described it as widely distributed in woodland whereas in recent years it has been noted at low density or casually only in the Brentwood area—at Brentwood in 1947 (*Proc. S. Lond. ent. nat. Hist. Soc.*, 1947–8:63), Thorndon Park in 1965 (RRC), Coxtie Green in 1974 (PJW) and Ingrave (KWG); at Witham (*Essex Nat.*, 31:110) and Dovercourt (MEA) in 1962; at Epping in 1964 (AME); at Langdon Hills (RT) and Wickham Bishops (GCD) in 1970–71; at Bradwell on-Sea where it is scarce and irregular (AJD); and on Danbury Ridge where it occurs in small numbers annually (GAP).

*Eustrotia bankiana* F. (Silver Bars)
This extremely local British species has been recorded only twice in Essex—single specimens at Bradwell-on-Sea on 21 June 1970 (AJD) and in the interior of the county in July of the same year (locality and recorder's name withheld).

*Eustrotia uncula* Clerck (Silver Hook)
A small colony of this local species was discovered towards the

west side of the county in 1955 and was still extant in 1958 (locality and recorder's name withheld). The only other record is of one at Bradwell-on-Sea on 31 July 1951 (AJD).

*Catocala fraxini* L. (Clifden Nonpareil)

Very rare visitor. This magnificent insect, the largest British noctuid, sometimes called the Blue Underwing, has been recorded in the county on at least four occasions. The VCH recounts that two specimens were taken at Southend-on-Sea in 1846 and one at Colchester in 1869. Subsequently one was found at Westcliff-on-Sea in September 1933 (HCH) and another at rest in a war-time gun emplacement at Frinton-on-Sea in late summer 1942 (HFDE). Additionally there seems little reason to doubt a record of one which appeared briefly at a sugar patch in Thorndon Park in the 1920s (R. G. Williment *per* EFW).

*Catocala nupta* L. (Red Underwing)

This large and handsome species is generally distributed and still quite common in a number of districts although it seems to have become rather scarce in others. An example of the rare ab. *caerulescens* Cockerell with blue on the hind-wings was taken at Walton-on-the-Naze in September 1937 (*Entomologist*, 75:63). A specimen with brown hind-wings was reported at Colchester in the 1950s (DC).

*Catocala sponsa* L. (Dark Crimson Underwing)

Very rare vagrant. One was once taken at Hainault (VCH) and another occurred at Bradwell-on-Sea on 12 September 1951 (AJD).

*Minucia lunaris* Schiff. (Lunar Double-stripe)

There would appear to have been a small influx of this fine moth in 1951 as one was obtained at Bradwell-on-Sea on 25 May (AJD) and two larvae were found at Hadleigh in early July of that year (HCH). The only other record concerns another at Bradwell-on-Sea on 1 June 1959 (AJD).

*Parellelia algira* L. (Passenger)

An example of this handsome Mediterranean species, only once previously recorded in the British Isles (near Dover, Kent), came to light at Bradwell-on-Sea on 15 September 1969 (AJD).

*Euclidia mi* Clerck (Mother Shipton)

Local. The VCH described this day-flying species as common on the coast but gave only one inland locality—the Colchester area—although there are other old records from Ongar, Epping Forest and Danbury and doubtless it occurred elsewhere in the interior. Today it cannot be said to be numerous anywhere and is still pre-dominantly coastal, occurring in at least 12 localities from Mistley round to Mucking. Inland it is decidedly local, having been reported in recent years only from five localities around Colchester (JF), Weeley (*Essex Nat.*, 31:110), Danbury Ridge (GAP),

Chigwell/Lambourne (IS), Hatfield Forest (CM, GHBS), and, in June 1971, from Plaistow in east London (WLC).

*Ectypa glyphica* L. (Burnet Companion)
Local. The VCH mentioned Epping and Southend-on-Sea as localities for this small day-flier but claimed that it was not found in the northern part of the county. As the compiler lived at Colchester it seems likely that some, at least, of the colonies reported in recent years from Berechurch, Stanway, West Bergholt and Fordham Heath (JF) did not then exist. Elsewhere colonies are reported from Danbury Ridge (GAP), Ramsden Bellhouse (PF), Hadleigh/Benfleet Downs (DGD, HCH), Thorndon Park (KWG), Grays Chalk Quarry N.R. (GAP), Chigwell/Lambourne (IS) and Hatfield Forest (PBMA, GHBS).

*Colocasia coryli* L. (Nut-tree Tussock)
Local. The VCH stated that this moth was fairly common among birch and beech. If this was ever the case then the species is much less widespread today. Epping Forest and the woods near Blackmore are its county strongholds: in the former area it was noted in 1937 (*Entomologist*, 71:27), 1947 (*Essex Nat.*, 28:79), 1968 (AME) and 1974 (DJLA), while in the latter it is common in Fryerning Wood (RRC, RT) and also occurs in High Woods (RRC). The only other records during the past half-century are: Boreham, two, 1930 (W. P. Seabrook coll.); Bradwell-on-Sea, May 1971 (AJD); Lexden, Colchester, August 1958 and May 1959 (JF); Wickham Bishops, 1969–71 (GCD); Hadleigh, scarce (HCH); Thorndon Park, scarce (PCF); Margaretting (RT) and Coxtie Green (PJW), May 1971; Ashdon (RJR); Hamford Water, June 1972 (JBF); Wrabness, two, August 1974 (MEA).

*Episema caerulocephala* L. (Figure of Eight)
The VCH described this autumn species as 'abounding everywhere'. It is still very widespread but is nowhere abundant, although fairly common in some districts.

*Polychrisia moneta* F. (Golden Plusia)
Widely distributed. First recorded in England in 1890, this moth, which is also called the Silver Eight, was first noted in Essex, at South Woodford, in 1893 (*Entomologist* 28:310; *Essex Nat.*, 7: 107 & 127). It is now widespread in the county, frequenting gardens and nurseries where its food-plants *Aconitum* (Monkshood) and *Delphinium* (Larkspur) are grown.

*Plusia chrysitis* L. (Burnished Brass)
This well-known and striking species is generally distributed and common in many districts, especially those containing extensive areas of rank vegetation.

*Plusia festucae* L. (Gold Spot)
Local and scarce. The VCH described it as scarce and gave Benfleet, Colchester, Maldon and St. Osyth as localities. The only

subsequent records are: Loughton, two, 1935 (*London Nat.*, 35: 67); Bradwell-on-Sea, has occurred in 15 years since 1947 but only once (in 1971) since 1965 (AJD); Chelmsford, 1947 (W. P. Seabrook coll.); Westcliff-on-Sea, 1–2 most years up to 1951 (HCH); Great Maplestead, one on 25 August 1960 (BWJP); Benfleet, one in August 1973 (JEC); Wix, one on 28 August 1974 (RM). There is no evidence that the recently separated *Plusia gracilis* Lempke (Lempke's Gold Spot) has ever occurred in Essex.

*Plusia jota* L. (Plain Golden Y)
Widespread. According to the VCH this plusia, though widely distributed, was generally scarce at the turn of the century. It may, therefore, have increased as today it seems to be almost universally distributed and is fairly common in a number of districts.

*Plusia pulchrina* Haw. (Beautiful Golden Y)
Widespread. The VCH gave only three localities for this attractive moth but felt it might well be widely distributed. At present this is certainly the case as although it is markedly less widespread than its close relative, *P. jota* (above), there are recent records from 20 widely scattered localities. In a few of them it is fairly common but in the majority it occurs only at low density.

*Plusia ni* Hübn. (Ni Moth)
Also called the Silver V, this immigrant has occurred in Essex only in 1958 when four examples were noted at Bradwell-on-Sea between 7 and 15 August (AJD) and one at Westcliff-on-Sea on 18 August (HCH).

*Plusia limbirena* Guen. (Scarbank Gem)
The second British specimen of this African and Asiatic species was taken at Bradwell-on-Sea on 27 September 1951 (AJD).

*Plusia confusa* Steph. (Dewick's Plusia)
The first British example of this Mediterranean species appeared at Bradwell-on-Sea on 3 October 1951 (AJD). A second occurred at the same place on 20 August 1955 (AJD) at a time when several others were recorded in various parts of the country.

*Plusia gamma* L. (Silver Y)
Very common. This well-known moth is far and away our commonest immigrant and in most years penetrates in numbers to all parts of the county. As would be expected it is most numerous on the coast where in some years it is abundant. It is probably less numerous today than formerly. The VCH recounts how, in 1900, near Clacton-on-Sea, the moths 'rose in clouds at nearly every step for several miles' but some recent accounts are most impressive. Examples are those of 7,398 in a light trap at Bradwell-on-Sea on 19 September 1960 (AJD) and, in August 1969, an estimated 100,000 at Colne Point N.R. (FDB, BH) and countless thousands at The Naze where two or three dozen were feeding at a single plant of *Ballota nigra* (Black Horehound) (GAP, JKW).

The diminutive race *gammina* Staud. appears in small numbers in most years and occasionally, as in 1973, when two occurred on Danbury Ridge (GAP), a few penetrate well inland.

*Plusia interrogationis* L. (Scarce Silver Y)

This northern British insect visited Essex as a continental immigrant in 1955 and in three later years. In 1955 a total of seven was noted at Bradwell-on-Sea between 28 July and 14 August inclusive (AJD) and one at Hockley on 29 July (DM). Subsequently single examples appeared at Westcliff-on-Sea on 2 August 1959 (HCH) and at Bradwell-on-Sea on 13 August 1960 and 30 July 1972 (AJD).

*Unca triplasia* L. (Dark Spectacle)

Apparently very local and scarce. The VCH recorded this moth from Brentwood, Epping, Harwich and Maldon, and several other localities are mentioned in the old literature. Today it appears to be very scarce and extremely local but the situation is confused as a result of frequent changes in the binomial nomenclature of both this and the next species and also by the tendency to melanism which is now exhibited by *U. tripartita*, some examples of which are as dark as *U. triplasia*. The only recent records regarded as entirely free from doubt are of two at Westcliff-on-Sea in June 1953 (HCH) and a few in most years at Bradwell-on-Sea (AJD).

*Unca tripartita* Hufn. (Light Spectacle)

Generally distributed. The VCH described this species as generally distributed but not common. It is still to be found in all districts and may have increased as it can fairly be described as numerous in some areas. As stated above, it is showing an increasing tendency to melanism.

*Acontia luctuosa* Schiff. (Four-spotted)

Rare. According to the VCH this attractive dusky and white, mainly day-flying species had occurred at Grays and Benfleet, and 'somewhat freely' at Maldon and Mucking in 1900. It occurred in small numbers at Westcliff-on-Sea (HCH) and on the Benfleet/ Hadleigh Downs up to 1948 (DGD, HCH) and irregularly at Bradwell-on-Sea up to 1958 (AJD), but otherwise has been noted, singly, during the past half-century only at Chelmsford *c*. 1936 (W.P. Seabrook coll.), Maldon on 1 August 1948 (GAP), West Mersea on 10 July 1954 (JF, CWS) and Ingrave on 17 July 1972 (KWG). The probability is that the species occasionally wanders across the Thames from the Kentish chalk downs and once in a while establishes itself temporarily in the county.

*Lygephila pastinum* Treits. (Blackneck)

Local. Recorded by the VCH only from Leigh-on-Sea, this quietly coloured yet distinctive species is now fairly widespread (in 20 known localities) east of a line Grays-Ongar-Manningtree but has yet to be recorded further west. It may still be in the process of extending its range, however, as at both Ongar and Stondon

Massey it is considered to have increased recently (DCT). In most of its haunts it occurs only at low density and is not really numerous anywhere.

*Rivula sericealis* Scop. (Straw Dot)

Local. Recorded in the VCH only from Colchester, Maldon, Rainham and Southend-on-Sea, this small moth, known also as the Straw Point, has been noted in a dozen localities in recent years. It is described as common in the Rochford Hundred (DGD, HCH), not uncommon on Thames-side (RT), fairly common at Bradwell-on-Sea (AJD), widely distributed in small numbers on Danbury Ridge and in the Chelmer Valley, Little Baddow (GAP), fairly common in Hatfield Forest (PBMA, CC, GHBS), resident at Stondon Massey (DCT) and occasional at Hookend (RRC) and Dovercourt (MEA). It was also noted at Debden in July 1967 (AME), Great Holland Pits N.R. in August 1971 (GAP, JKW) and near Takeley in July 1972 (GHBS).

*Phytometra viridaria* Clerck (Small Purple Bars)

Rare and very local. The VCH described this pretty day-flying species as common at Epping and as formerly occurring at Dedham, while the literature gives Ongar and several places around Maldon as other former localities. At the present time it is known only in the Hadleigh/Thundersley district where it is uncommon (DGD, HCH), although it was described as abundant at Hadleigh in 1931–32 (EFW). A straggler occurred at Bradwell-on-Sea on 1 August 1951 (AJD).

*Parascotia fuliginaria* L. (Waved Black)

Rare. The VCH gave only one record of this blackish species—at Hale End, Walthamstow, in 1901. Since then single specimens have been noted at Bradwell-on-Sea on 19 August 1959, 10 August 1972, 3 August 1973 and 29 July 1974 (AJD), on Thames-side on 23 July 1967 (RT) and at Thundersley on 6 August 1969 (DGD).

*Scoliopteryx libratrix* L. (Herald)

This most attractive and unusually coloured species is generally distributed and fairly common in many areas.

*Hypena proboscidalis* L. (Common Snout)

Common generally and at times abounding in extensive nettle patches.

*Hypena rostralis* L. (Buttoned Snout)

Very local and increasingly scarce in its one remaining stronghold. This species must have decreased disastrously after the turn of the century as the VCH stated that it 'abounded among hops' whereas there is only one record between then and 1925—of one at Ingrave in September 1923 (EFW)—and, apart from single specimens at Bradwell-on-Sea on 12 June 1954 and 10 July 1974 (AJD) and Dovercourt on 15 September 1964 (MEA), it has been noted since only in the Rochford Hundred where it was common up to the mid-1950s but is now scarce and local (DGD, HCH).

The next two insects, together with *Hypenodes turfosalis* Hocke (the Marsh Oblique-barred Snout) which has not yet been recorded for Essex, are insignificant little brown insects which are easily overlooked and could well be mistaken for 'micros'. It follows that the undermentioned records may well not reflect the true status of either species.

*Schrankia taenialis* Hübn. (White-line Snout)
Epping and Brentwood are the only localities mentioned in the VCH and in late years it has been found only at Creeksea where it occurred until 1964 when the wood it frequented was destroyed (HCH), and at Bradwell-on-Sea on 21 July 1967 and 20 July 1971 (AJD).

*Schrankia costaestrigalis* Steph. (Pinion-streaked Snout)
The VCH gave Epping and Hazeleigh as localities for this moth. It has occurred in nine years between 1956 and 1973 inclusive at Bradwell-on-Sea (AJD), is to be found sparingly at Hadleigh (DGD, HCH) and formerly occurred in a Creeksea wood which was grubbed out in 1964 (HCH). The only other record concerns one close to marshy ground at Sandon near Chelmsford *c.* 1970 (RG).

*Trisateles emortualis* Schiff. (Olive Crescent)
This exceedingly rare British moth was taken at Epping Forest in June 1859 and in the same area, at Loughton, again in 1870 (VCH; *Lond. Nat.*, 35:74). No more was seen of the species in Essex until 1970 when a presumed immigrant occurred at Bradwell-on-Sea on 27 June (AJD). More recently, on 8 August 1972, one was discovered in a wood in the northern half of the county and a second was found there on 24 August 1974 (locality and recorder's name withheld).

*Zanclognatha tarsipennalis* Treits. (Brown Fanfoot)
Widespread. The VCH stated that this fanfoot was of general occurrence. Still widely distributed it has been noted in 19 localities, in some of which it is common.

*Zanclognatha nemoralis* F. (Small Fanfoot)
Widespread. This diminutive fanfoot was also said by the VCH to occur generally and, like *Z. tarsipennalis* (above), it is still widely distributed and locally common. If anything it is the more widespread of the two species.

*Zanclognatha cribrumalis* Hübn. (Dotted Fanfoot)
Local. The VCH recorded it only from Leigh-on-Sea, Mucking and Walton-on-Naze but it is now known to occur at 14 points around the coast and estuaries from Dovercourt to Thames-side, in several of which it is common. It has been noted in only two

inland localities—in the Chelmer Valley N.R., Little Baddow, where it is fairly common (GAP) and at Thorndon Park/Ingrave where it is scarce (PCF, KWG).

*Paracolax derivalis* Hübn. (Clay Fanfoot)

Very local and scarce; not recorded during the past decade. It is difficult to tell from the VCH precisely what was the status of this moth at the turn of the century: however, only two specific localities are mentioned—Colchester and Leigh-on-Sea. Additionally there is a record of one at Harwich in 1911 (*Entomologist*, 45: 203). The W. P. Seabrook collection contains single specimens from Chelmsford (1926) and Colchester (1947) but otherwise it is recorded in recent years only from Bradwell-on-Sea in 1948, 1950 and 1958 (AJD) and from Rochford and Hadleigh up to 1959 (DGD, HCH).

*Herminia barbalis* Clerck (Common Fanfoot)

Despite its vernacular name this fanfoot is now very local and scarce. It would appear to have declined disastrously during this century as the VCH described it as generally distributed and common in woods, although one wonders whether there has always been some confusion (as there is today) between this species and *Z. tarsipennalis* (above) which is frequently referred to in the vernacular as 'the Fanfoot'. In the south-east it is found at low density at Canewdon (HCH), was scarce at Creeksea until 1964 when its habitat was destroyed (HCH) and occurred up to 1952 at Thundersley (DGD). In the north single specimens were noted at Lamarsh on 18 July 1970 and at Earls Colne on 3 June 1971 (FDB: CNHS). There are no other recent records.

*Laspeyria flexula* Schiff. (Beautiful Hook-tip)

Widely distributed. The VCH termed this attractive species as scarce and gave only four localities—Colchester, Halstead, Langham, and Hazeleigh near Maldon. Today it is known to be widespread: noted in some 20 localities, it is fairly common in a few but scarce or very scarce in most.

*Archiearis parthenias* L. (Orange Underwing)

Fairly widespread. The VCH mentioned five known localities for this attractive day-flier of the early spring and thought it would be found in most large woods among birch. This is probably true today although, of course, there are fewer sizeable areas of woodland now than at the beginning of the century and a number of them, through lack of management, do not have the open spaces which this species needs. Nevertheless there are recent records from Ramsey in the north-east (ICR), East Donyland, West Bergholt and Berechurch (JF), parts of the Rochford Hundred (HCH), Danbury Ridge (GAP), parts of the Brentwood district (RRC, PCF, EFW) and Hatfield Forest (PBMA, CC), while it was noted in the now much overgrown Hazeleigh Wood, near Maldon, in 1938 (GAP).

It is still fairly common in several of these localities but there have been recent signs of a decline in some areas.

*Archiearis notha* Hübn. (Light Orange Underwing)

Local. This species, which closely resembles the last in appearance and habits but is on the wing rather later in the spring and feeds on aspen, has always been scarce and more local than *A. parthenias* although the VCH stated that it occurred in 'many' woods. It was plentiful in Ongar Park Woods in 1933 and stated to be present (no date) at Epping (*London Nat.*, 36:60) but more recently it has been reported only from: East Donyland, April 1956–58 (JF); Benfleet and Hadleigh, not uncommon locally (HCH); and, in the north-west, at Quendon where it was found to be common on 29–30 March 1965 (AME).

*Alsophila aescularia* Schiff. (March Moth)

Generally distributed and numerous in many areas.

*Aplasta ononaria* Fuessl. (Rest-harrow)

The only Essex record of this moth is of one at Bradwell-on-Sea on 2 September 1961 (AJD); presumably it was either an immigrant or had wandered from one of the colonies on the Kent coast.

*Pseudoterpna pruinata* Hufn. (Grass Emerald)

Rather local. The VCH stated that this green moth with a blue-grey tinge was of general occurrence among broom and gorse, its food-plants. Today it is chiefly found, at low density, in the vicinity of the coast and estuaries along which it has been noted in some 12 localities from Dovercourt round to Mucking. The only inland records since 1925 are: Danbury Ridge, fairly common (GAP); Warley, larva *c.* 1932 (*Proc. S. Lond. ent. nat. Hist Soc.*, 1932–3:84); Thorndon Park/Ingrave, scarce (PCF, KWG); Tiptree Heath, August 1969 (GAP). It is also recorded, without date, from Epping Forest (*London Nat.*, 36:60).

*Geometra papilionaria* L. (Large Emerald)

Widely distributed. The VCH described this fine insect as scarce but as occurring in many places. The same can be said of it at the present time as it is recorded, mainly at low density, from many localities all over the county. Nowhere really common, it is however fairly numerous in some of the more extensive woodland areas which contain plenty of birch and hazel.

*Comibaena pustulata* Hufn. (Blotched Emerald)

Widely distributed. This attractive emerald was stated in the VCH to occur 'in nearly all oak woods' and to have increased of late years. It is still widespread, having been reported from 21 widely scattered localities, and is fairly common in some districts where oak is plentiful.

*Hemithia aestivaria* Hübn. (Common Emerald)

Generally distributed and common.

*Thetidia smaragdaria* F. (Essex Emerald)

Very local; much decreased. This beautiful pale green moth, which bears the county's name, is now found in Britain only on the south-east coast and estuaries and may now be confined to Essex where it was discovered as a British insect, at Southchurch, near Southend-on-Sea, in 1826. The larvae feed on *Artemesia maritima* (Sea-wormwood) growing on the edge of the saltings. It has become extremely local and scarce, due partly to the activities of collectors and partly to the wholesale destruction of the food-plant by the extensive strengthening of sea-walls following the east coast floods of 1953. Even at the turn of the century the VCH expressed fears that the insect had been 'much too keenly worked for of late by the London and other collectors' and the less that is said about its past and present Essex haunts the better. Clearly, however, its continued existence as a British species is at risk and the utmost restraint should be exercised in collecting it. All records should be notified to the Essex Naturalists' Trust.

*Thalera fimbrialis* Scop. (Sussex Emerald)

An example of this rare British moth, presumably an immigrant, was taken at Bradwell-on-Sea on 8 August 1946 (AJD).

*Hemistola immaculata* Thunb. (Lesser Emerald)

Rather local. The VCH described this emerald as somewhat local, but not uncommon among *Clematis vitalba* (Traveller's Joy). Its present-day status is similar as it is recorded from 22 localities, in some of which it is quite common, spread over much of the county, although it is absent from or occurs only as a vagrant in a few quite extensive areas, e.g. east-central Essex and parts of the coast, where its food-plant does not grow. It seems to be most widespread in west and north-west Essex and around Colchester.

*Jodis lactearia* L. (Little Emerald)

Widespread at varying density. The VCH considered this delicate little moth to be 'common in woods and lanes everywhere'. Though still widely distributed it is certainly no longer universally numerous and in a few localities it has not been seen recently. Unless, therefore, it has been overlooked in some areas it would seem that over the county as a whole it has declined in numbers in late years.

*Calothysanis amata* L. (Blood-vein)

Generally distributed and common. Melanic examples have been taken on Danbury Ridge (GAP) and at Bradwell-on-Sea (AJD).

*Cosymbia albipunctata* Hufn. (Birch Mocha)

Rather local and generally uncommon, as was the case when the VCH was written. A birch woodland species, it is widespread at Berechurch, Lexden, West Bergholt and Copford (JF), fairly common in some years on Danbury Ridge (GAP), very scarce and irregular at Bradwell-on-Sea (AJD), rather scarce at Hadleigh,

Benfleet and Thundersley in the south-east (DGD, HCH), fairly common at Blackmore (RRC, RT), present at Thorndon Park/ Ingrave (PCF, KWG) and occasional at Stondon Massey (DCT). Additionally single examples occurred at Chelmsford in 1965 (GAP), at Chigwell Row in 1973 (IS) and in Epping Forest in 1974 (NE). There are no recent records for the west or north-west.

*Cosymbia annulata* Schultze (Mocha)

Very local. The VCH stated that this species, which is also known as the Maple Mocha, occurred freely in many places, especially on the boulder clay towards the north-west of the county. There are no present-day records for the latter area, which, however, is greatly under-recorded. Its only remaining stronghold seems to be the Colchester district where it is described as locally common at Lexden, Copford, Donyland, Berechurch, West Bergholt and Great Horkesley (JF). The only other post-1925 records are: Rochford, very scarce (HCH); Ugley, 10 May 1947 (CC); Great Maplestead, 25 May 1970 (BWJP).

*Cosymbia puppillaria* Hübn. (Blair's Mocha)

First recognised as British when a specimen was taken on the Isle of Wight in 1946, this extremely rare species has occurred only once in Essex, a female having come to light at Hockley on 23 May 1956 (DM; *Ent. Rec.*, 82:96 & 99).

*Cosymbia porata* L. (False Mocha)

Once widely distributed, now very local and scarce. The VCH stated that it occurred freely among scrub oak at the turn of the century but recently it has been recorded only at Bradwell-on-Sea in five years between 1947 and 1956 inclusive (AJD), in the Rochford Hundred where it was common up to the mid-1950s but is now scarce (DGD, HCH), occasionally at Stondon Massey (DCT), and at Dovercourt on 27 August 1971 (MEA).

*Cosymbia punctaria* L. (Maiden's Blush)

Local. Formerly, according to the VCH, of similar status to the last species, *C. punctaria* has also declined, although not to the same extent as *C. porata*. It occurred at Bradwell-on-Sea in five years between 1948 and 1954 inclusive (AJD), is becoming scarce in the Rochford Hundred where it was common up to the mid-1950s (DGD, HCH), still occurs regularly near Colchester at Lexden, Berechurch and Copford (JF) and was fairly common on Galleywood Common in June 1964 (GAP). It has also been noted lately at Mayland (PCF), Thorndon Park/Ingrave (PCF, KWG), Margaretting (GAP) and Danbury Ridge (GAP).

*Cosymbia linearia* Hübn. (Clay Triple-lines)

Decidedly local. The VCH gave only one locality for this moth, namely Epping Forest where it was said to be plentiful among beech. It has since been recorded on numerous occasions from this district where it doubtless still occurs, although the most recent record appears to be May 1961 (HEC). It is also present in small numbers in Thorndon Park (PCF) and at Coxtie Green (PJW). Additionally it is found around Colchester where it is common among planted beech at Lexden, Donyland, Berechurch, Fordham and Great Horkesley (JF). It may have established itself here during the present century as the VCH was well informed about the Lepidoptera of the Colchester district. It has occurred at Bradwell-on-Sea in six years since 1950 (AJD). An example of the very rare ab. *fasciata* Prout, with smoky bands across the wings, taken in Epping Forest, was exhibited in 1926 (*Entomologist*, 59: 175 & 210).

*Scopula promutata* Guen. (Mullein Wave)
Local. This wave is mainly confined to the coast and its vicinity and the VCH's 'widely distributed' should presumably be read in this context. It is still widespread but at mostly rather low density around the coast and estuaries, having been noted recently in about a dozen localities between Dovercourt and Thames-side. It is fairly common in Thorndon Park (PCF) but otherwise records from North Ockendon in 1963 (DCT), Coxtie Green in 1972 (PJW), Wickham Bishops in 1969–71 (GCD) and Kingsford Bridge Marsh N.R., Layer-de-la-Haye, in 1974 (FDB:CNHS, JF) represent its further penetrations inland.

*Scopula ornata* Scop. (Lace-border)
The only Essex records of this species come from Leigh-on-Sea in 1893 (VCH), Bradwell-on-Sea on 13 August 1950 (AJD) and West Bergholt in June 1957 (JF). All were probably wanderers from the southern chalk downs.

*Scopula imitaria* Hübn. (Small Blood-vein)
Widespread at varying density. The VCH referred to this species as generally common but it appears no longer to be universally distributed although it is still to be found in many districts. In some areas where it does occur it is scarce and there are few places where it can be described as really common.

*Scopula emutaria* Hübn. (Rosy Wave)
This most attractive pink-tinged wave is widely distributed along the coast and estuaries as it was said to be by the VCH, frequenting especially the edges of saltings. Occurring in Essex as ab. *subroseata* Haw., it has been noted of late in small to moderate numbers in 15 localities from Harwich round to Benfleet.

*Scopula immutata* L. (Lesser Cream Wave)
Local. It is surprising that the VCH gave only Southend and Leigh-on-Sea as localities for this species as with the widespread drainage of marshes it can hardly have extended its range during the present century, yet it has been noted in 15 localities, mostly on the eastern side of the county, in recent years. In the north-east it is locally common at Donyland, Berechurch, Lexden and Copford

99

(JF) and occurred at Dovercourt (MEA) and Layer-de-la-Haye and Earls Colne (FDB:CNHS) in 1972. In the east and south it occurred at Bradwell-on-Sea in seven years between 1947 and 1959 inclusive (AJD) and on Danbury Ridge in 1974 (GAP), it is not uncommon locally at Rochford and Benfleet (HCH), and is scarce at Thundersley (DGD), on Thames-side (RRC, RT) and on Langdon Hills (RT). On the west side it was noted in Hatfield Forest from 1951–55 and again in 1974 (GHBS).

*Scopula lactata* Haw. (Cream Wave)
Not as widespread as when the VCH referred to it as generally common, this wave is best described today as well distributed at varying density in most heavily timbered districts.

*Sterrha ochrata* Scop. (Bright Wave)
Rare. This extremely local British species, alternatively known as the Pale Ochraceous Wave, was recorded by the VCH from Southend-on-Sea and St. Osyth. It is now to be found in only one (coastal) area where it is strictly protected (locality and recorders' names withheld).

*Sterrha vulpinaria* H.-S. (Least Carpet)
Still local, but has increased and extended its range considerably. This wave, always regarded as a very local species in Britain, had not long been discovered in Essex, in the Southend-on-Sea district (actually Shoeburyness), when the VCH was published. Now widespread on and near the Thames estuary, it is generally distributed and locally quite common in the Rochford Hundred (DGD, HCH) and present in small numbers on Thames-side (RT; *Ent. Rec.*, 67:47) and at Grays Chalk Quarry N.R. (RT), while one was noted at Horndon-on-the-Hill in July 1953 (*Ent. Rec.*, 67:47) and it is common at Hornchurch (WLC). On the coast it was first noted in 1958 at Bradwell-on-Sea where it occurs in small numbers most years (AJD) and it has since spread to Hamford Water (JBF) and Dovercourt (MEA) where occasional specimens have occurred since 1964. It has also penetrated well inland, viz., Ingrave/Thorndon Park, fairly common (PCF, KWG); Coxtie Green, occasional, 1972–73 (PJW); Harold Hill, common (WLC); Collier Row, Romford, quite common, July 1968 (RRC); Ongar, occasional (DCT); Danbury Ridge, 1–2 most years since 1968 (GAP); Tiptree, one in June 1970 (FDB).

*Sterrha interjectaria* Boisd. (Dwarf Cream Wave)
Fairly widespread. The VCH described this small species as generally common but at present, unless overlooked or under-recorded, it is decidedly local on the west side of the county although widely distributed and frequently common in the east.

*Sterrha dimidiata* Hufn. (Single-dotted Wave)
Widely distributed and common in a number of localities.

*Sterrha seriata* Schrank (Small Dusty Wave)
   Generally distributed and common.
*Sterrha subsericeata* Haw. (Satin Wave)
   Local. According to the VCH this glossy wave was somewhat
   local but was to be found more freely in the south than in the north
   of the county. Today it seems to be confined to the eastern half of
   Essex: there it is local and scarce at Westcliff-on-Sea and Hadleigh
   (HCH); common on Danbury Ridge (GAP); and present near Colchester at Lexden, West Bergholt, Berechurch and Donyland (JF)
   and at Dovercourt where 1–2 have occurred almost annually since
   1967 (MEA). Odd specimens were noted at Bradwell-on-Sea in
   1964 (AJD) and at Benfleet in 1972 (JC).
*Sterrha straminata* Borkh. (Plain Wave)
   Local and scarce. The VCH stated that this species was 'found
   frequently in woods'. Either it has become much scarcer or, because of its close similarity to the next species, it is overlooked
   nowadays as the only records during the last half-century are:
   Danbury Ridge, regular but rather scarce (GAP); Bradwell-on-Sea,
   apparently scarce and irregular (AJD); Hadleigh, very scarce
   (HCH); Ingrave/Thorndon Park, small numbers (PCF, KWG); Ongar
   Park Woods, July 1929 (*Entomologist*, 63:42); Wickham Bishops,
   1970 (GCD); Thundersley, one, 17 July 1972 (JC).
*Sterrha aversata* L. (Riband Wave)
   Common everywhere, approaching abundance in some districts.
*Sterrha trigeminata* Haw. (Treble Brown-spot)
   Widespread. According to the VCH this distinctive wave was
   scarcer than *S. dimidiata* (above) and *S. biselata* (below) but was
   to be found in many areas. Its status does not, therefore, seem to
   have changed much as it has been noted in more than 20 localities
   in recent years and is fairly common in several. It is regarded as a
   distinctly local species in Great Britain and is probably as well
   represented in Essex as in any county.
*Sterrha biselata* Hufn. (Small Fan-footed Wave)
   Widespread in well-timbered areas and very common in some
   woods.
*Sterrha emarginata* L. (Small Scallop)
   Widely distributed. The VCH described this species as very
   common, but although still widespread it is now to be found only
   at low density in some areas and is common in few; preferring
   damp localities it has probably suffered from the effects of land
   drainage.
*Rhodometra sacraria* L. (Vestal)
   Irregular immigrant. The VCH gave only one record, from
   Colchester, of this attractive little immigrant but two other late
   19th century occurrences are mentioned in the literature. Apparently no other visitations were reported until 1947, an exceptional

year for the species, when it was not uncommon on part of Foulness Island in September (HCH), eight occurred at Bradwell-on-Sea (AJD), and one was found inland at Great Waltham on 28 September (*Essex Nat.*, 28:79). Subsequent records are: Great Bardfield, 2 September 1958 (*Essex Nat.*, 30:208); Bradwell-on-Sea, 1959 (2), 1961, 1963, 1964 (3) and 1971 (AJD); Westcliff-on-Sea, 19 October 1959 (HCH); Ongar, 15 September 1961 (DCT); Hockley (3), 17–20 September 1961 (DM); Stondon Massey (3), 25 October 1963 (DCT); Thames-side (2), 27–28 September 1967 (RT).

*Xanthorhoe quadrifasiata* Clerck (Large Twin-spot Carpet)

Local and scarce. This fine carpet was said by the VCH to be scarce but well distributed. It is still found in a number of localities but most are in the south and west. In the south-east it is scarce at Rochford, Benfleet and Hadleigh (HCH) and in the south occasional on Thames-side and Langdon Hills and regular in small numbers at Grays Chalk Quarry N.R. (RT); in east-central Essex a few are seen annually on Danbury Ridge (GAP) and in the east it occurred at Bradwell-on-Sea in the late 1930s and in 1971 and 1973 (AJD). In the west one was seen a few yards outside the county boundary on Sawbridgeworth Marsh N.R. in 1971 (GAP), while it was reported from Hatfield Forest in 1969 and 1972, and from Takeley in 1973 and Widdington in 1974 (GHBS); and in the north one was taken at Great Maplestead in 1961 (BWJP).

*Xanthorhoe ferrugata* Clerck (Dark Twin-spot Carpet)

Generally distributed and common.

*Xanthorhoe spadicearia* Schiff. (Red Twin-spot Carpet)

While lacking the universal distribution of *X. ferrugata* the present species is still very widespread and common in a number of districts.

*Xanthorhoe designata* Hufn. (Flame Carpet)

Very local. The VCH gave West Bergholt, Great Tey, Langham and 'near Harwich', all in north Essex, as localities but the old literature mentions others in the east and south-west. At the present time it seems to be virtually confined to the Rochford Hundred (HCH) and the Colchester area—Lexden, Berechurch and Donyland (JF)—in both of which it is said to be quite common locally. The only other records in the last half-century concern single specimens at Maylands, Romford, on 17 April 1943 (EFW) and at Bradwell-on-Sea on 15 August 1960 and 16 August 1973 (AJD), and two at Dovercourt in August 1973 (MEA).

*Xanthorhoe montanata* Schiff. (Silver-ground Carpet)

Generally distributed and common.

*Xanthorhoe fluctuata* L. (Garden Carpet)

Also generally distributed and common.

*Nycterosea obstipata* F. (Gem)

Fairly regular immigrant. The VCH stated that this diminutive

102

species, also known as the Narrow-barred Carpet, was rare, having been reported only from Colchester and five places in south Essex. It is now known as a scarce, though almost annual, immigrant reported from Bradwell-on-Sea, where 34 appeared in 1961 and 25 in 1969 but otherwise 1–16 (AJD); the Rochford Hundred (HCH) and Thames-side (RT); and occasionally Dovercourt/Hamford Water (MEA, JBF). Inland it has been noted recently only on Danbury Ridge, in 1969 (GAP).

*Colostygia pectinataria* Knoch (Green Carpet)
Local. The VCH described this carpet, so attractive when fresh, as occurring frequently in woods and lanes. Its distribution is now decidedly patchy as it has been noted of late at varying density in only a dozen or so well scattered localities, viz., Bradwell-on-Sea (AJD), the Rochford Hundred (HCH), Langdon Hills (RT), Thorndon Park (PCF), Danbury Ridge (GAP), Billericay (EFW), near Colchester at Lexden, Berechurch and Copford (JF), Felsted (MFW), Ongar (DCT), and Hatfield Forest and Widdington (GHBS).

*Colostygia multistrigaria* Haw. (Mottled Grey)
Very local and scarce. The VCH recorded this species, also known as the Grey Mottled Carpet, only from Epping, Wanstead and Hazeleigh, near Maldon, and there is a subsequent but undated record from the first-mentioned locality (*London Nat.*, 36:83). It has since been noted only at Hadleigh where it was found sparsely from 1934–36 (HCH), Ingrave/Thorndon Park on 15 April 1967 (KWG) and 24 March 1974 (WLC), Danbury Ridge (3) on 19 March 1971 (DGD), Blackmore (4–5) in April 1973 (WLC) and Epping Forest in 1974 (NE).

*Colostygia didymata* L. (Twin-spot Carpet)
Local and scarce. According to the VCH it was generally common at the turn of the century but Dr C. G. M. de Worms (*London Nat.*, 36:84) pointed out that a decrease in south and south-east England had become apparent by the mid-1950s. It certainly seems to be far less in evidence in Essex than formerly and the only recent records are: Bradwell-on-Sea, uncommon (AJD); Rochford Hundred, formerly common, now scarce (DGD, HCH); Thames-side, one, 1974 (RT); Langdon Hills, two, 1970 (RT); Thorndon Park/Ingrave, scarce (PCF, KWG); Danbury Ridge and Chelmer Valley, Little Baddow, scarce (GAP); Hatfield Forest, *c.* 1946 (BSCNHS); Walton-on-the-Naze, 1970 (JKW); Dovercourt, a few most years (MEA); Takeley, 1974 (GHBS).

*Earophila badiata* Schiff. (Shoulder-stripe)
Very widely, perhaps generally, distributed and common in a number of districts.

*Anticlea derivata* Schiff. (Streamer)
This well-marked species is rather less widely distributed than *E. badiata* (above) although found in a large number of districts, and

is much less numerous, being generally scarce or very scarce, as it was in the VCH's day.

*Mesoleuca albicillata* L. (Beautiful Carpet)

Local and generally scarce. This large carpet, so aptly named, was stated by the VCH to be widely distributed though far from common. The same can be said of it today, except that it is much less widespread. All recent records are given: Rochford Hundred, widely distributed but scarce (HCH); Grays Chalk Quarry N.R., July 1969 (RT); Danbury Ridge, rather scarce (GAP); Colchester district, local at Lexden, Berechurch, Fordham and West Bergholt (JF); Epping Forest, June 1947 (*Proc. S. Lond. ent. nat. Hist. Soc.*, 1947–8:64); Hatfield Forest, prior to 1950 (CC); Weeley, July 1963 (*Essex Nat.*, 31:113); Wickham Bishops, 1970 (GCD); Bradwell-on-Sea, July 1971 (SFJD); Dovercourt, 1972–73 (MEA); Coxtie Green, 1974 (PJW).

*Perizoma affinitata* Steph. (Large Rivulet)

Widely distributed and common in some districts.

*Perizoma alchemillata* L. (Small Rivulet)

Widely distributed. The VCH suggested that this rivulet occurred as freely as *P. affinitata* (above) but it is now less widespread than that species, although recorded from some 20 well-scattered localities, and generally markedly scarcer. It is, however, common in a few areas, notably on Danbury Ridge where in some years it is very numerous (GAP).

*Perizoma flavofasciata* Thunb. (Sandy Carpet)

Widely distributed and generally common.

*Perizoma albulata* Schiff. (Grass Rivulet)

Rare; not recorded in the past decade. Brentwood, Doddinghurst, Epping and Maldon were mentioned as localities in the VCH but subsequently it has only been recorded (once, undated) at Birchanger in the west (CM), in very small numbers annually at Benfleet up to 1939 (HCH), and at Bradwell-on-Sea from 1950–52 and in 1958 (AJD).

*Perizoma bifaciata* Haw. (Barred Rivulet)

Local. The VCH stated that this rivulet was sometimes common in north Essex on *Bartsia odontites* (Red Bartsia). This was probably a reference to the 'prodigious' numbers of larvae found in 1902 in the Harwich district (*Entomologist*, 36:141) and, indeed, this district is still apparently a stronghold of the species as larvae were noted in 1935 (HEC) and an imago in 1973 (MEA) at Dovercourt, while it was found in some abundance at Wrabness in July 1973 (MEA). Otherwise it appears to be well established only in the Rochford Hundred where it is locally common (DGD, HCH), although a few occur in most years at Bradwell-on-Sea (AJD). Other recent records are: Ongar, 1965 (DCT); Danbury Ridge, August 1969 and 1974 (GAP); Hatfield Forest and Debden,

August 1969 (GHBS); Wickham Bishops, 1971 (GCD); Thorndon Park, 1973 (PCF).

*Euphyia unangulata* Haw. (Sharp-angled Carpet)
Local. The VCH described this well-marked carpet as somewhat common locally and this is still the position. It is fairly widespread in north-east Essex where it is recorded from 10 localities and extends as far west as Lamarsh (FDB:CNHS); it has been found recently in four localities around Brentwood; and in east-central Essex it is common on Danbury Ridge (GAP), probably its Essex stronghold, and was recorded annually at Wickham Bishops from 1969–71 (GCD). In the east it occurred at Bradwell-on-Sea in seven years between 1947 and 1972 inclusive (AJD), but there are no records from the south-east, south or west of the county.

*Euphyia luctuata* Schiff. (White-banded Carpet)
A single example of this handsome carpet, which is established in Kent, discovered by J. Cosmo Melvil among a series of *E. unangulata* purchased from a Mr Gibbs, was said to have been taken at Woodham Ferrers (*Entomologist*, 61:51; *Proc. S. Lond. ent. nat. Hist. Soc.*, 1953–4:14). On 15 June 1974 a worn specimen came to light at Hookend (RRC). It is perhaps unlikely that the accidental release at Collier Row (8 miles sw.) *c.* 1969 of an impregnated female 'imported' from Kent has any bearing on the latter record.

*Euphyia picata* Hübn. (Cloaked Carpet)
Rare. Of this handsome species the VCH stated that it had a wide distribution but had been difficult to find since the great drought of 1893. It would seem that it never recovered from this setback as it has been recorded since only from Benfleet and Hadleigh where it was occasional up to 1938 (HCH), Dovercourt in July 1961 (MEA), and in another locality in north-east Essex in July 1973 (2) and August 1974 (2) (MEA).

*Euphyia cuculata* Hufn. (Royal Mantle)
The only Essex records of this species concern single examples in Epping Forest in May 1896 (VCH) and on Thames-side on 13 July 1966 and 4 July 1969 (RT), probably wanderers from the chalk downs south of the Thames.

*Euphyia rubidata* Schiff. (Ruddy Carpet)
Very local and scarce. The VCH stated that it was widely distributed and currently common following a long period of scarcity. It is obviously one of our sadly diminished species as the only records for the last half-century are: Hadleigh, a few annually up to 1939 (HCH); Bradwell-on-Sea, 1956 and 1959 (AJD); Thundersley, one on 21 June 1970 (DGD); Orsett, formerly common in woodland since destroyed by gravel workings (HCH); Thorndon Park, two on 29 June 1973 (PCF).

*Euphyia bilineata* L. (Yellow Shell)
Very common everywhere.

*Melanthia procellata* Schiff. (Pretty Chalk Carpet)

Fairly widely distributed at low density in *'Clematis'* districts, being found in several others where the food-plant is absent in the wild state. The VCH gave this attractive carpet as occurring near Colchester and at Southend-on-Sea and Harwich, but more recently it has been noted in over 20 widely scattered localities. It is, however, unknown south and west of lines drawn from Chelmsford to Waltham Abbey and to the Thames immediately west of Grays respectively, and is extremely local and scarce in the south-east. It is unlikely that a species of such universal scarcity in Essex has extended its range to the degree which the distribution given by the VCH suggests, and it is reasonable to assume that it was overlooked in earlier years. For an insect usually associated with chalk districts, as its name implies, its wide distribution in the county is unexpected.

*Mesotype virgata* Hufn. (Oblique-striped)

This species has been noted only twice in the county—at Bradwell-on-Sea on 29 August 1955 (AJD) and at Colne Point N.R. in June 1960 (JF).

*Lyncometra ocellata* L. (Purple Bar)

Fairly widespread at varying density. As the VCH described this pretty little moth as common everywhere it is fairly obvious that it has declined markedly during the present century. Reported in recent years from 18 well-timbered localities scattered throughout the county it is fairly common in some but scarce in others.

*Lampropteryx suffumata* Schiff. (Water Carpet)

Rather local. According to the VCH this handsome carpet of the late spring occurred freely at Epping and Maldon, in the Harwich district, and rarely at Colchester. Its range is now known to be less restricted than the VCH suggested but it is far from being generally distributed. It appears to be poorly represented in the western half of the county, having been noted in only five localities in recent years, but it is known to occur in 12 areas in the eastern part. There it seems to be extending its range as it is now established at Bradwell-on-Sea, where it first appeared in 1958 (AJD), and in 1974 it was noted for the first time at Wrabness where it was well represented (MEA) and at Wix (RM).

*Electrophaes corylata* Thunb. (Broken-barred Carpet)

Widely distributed over much of the county. The VCH considered this species to be common everywhere, but although it is still widespread and common in some districts, there do not seem to be any recent records for south Essex west of the Rochford Hundred, or apart from Ongar, the west side of the county.

*Ecliptopera silaceata* Schiff. (Small Phoenix)

Widely distributed and quite common locally. The VCH stated that this well-marked geometer was rare and had been found only at Colchester and Epping. It must, therefore, rank as one of our much increased species as it has been recorded in late years from over 20 localities spread through the county. There may well be a connection between its increase and extension of range and the spread of *Chamaenerion angustifolium* (Rosebay Willow-herb), one of its chief food-plants.

*Lygris prunata* L. (Large Phoenix)

Very local and scarce. According to the VCH this sizeable geometer had formerly been common at Epping and was to be found at Maldon, while there is an old record of its occurrence between Walton-on-the-Naze and Brightlingsea in 1842 (*Entomologist*, 1: 384). The only subsequent records are: Lexden (Colchester), local, July 1956–57 (JF); Saffron Walden, one in 1959, two in 1967 and one in 1968, all in July-August (AME); Dovercourt, single examples in 1969 and 1971 and three in 1972, all in July-August (MEA).

*Lygris testata* L. (Chevron)

Local. The VCH described this moth as of frequent occurrence among sallow and birch which suggests that it was then widely distributed. If this was the case then it has decreased markedly during the present century as the only subsequent records we can trace are: Bradwell-on-Sea, scarce and irregular (AJD); Benfleet, rare and local (HCH); Danbury Ridge, regular but scarce (GAP); Ongar, August 1965 (DCT); Felsted, two, 1968 (MFW); Debden, August 1969 (GHBS); Wickham Bishops, 1969–71 (GCD); Lamarsh, several, July 1970 (FDB:CNHS); Epping Forest, August 1971 (RRC); Fingringhoe Wick N.R., September 1971 (GAP); Hookend, 1974 (RRC).

*Lygris mellinata* F. (Spinach)

Primarily a frequenter of gardens and allotments containing currant bushes, this species is still very widely, if not generally, distributed, but it is doubtfully as common as when the VCH described it as occurring 'freely'.

*Lygris pyraliata* Schiff. (Barred Straw)

Generally distributed and common or fairly so.

*Cidaria fulvata* Forst. (Barred Yellow)

This most attractively coloured little moth is also generally distributed and is common in a number of districts.

*Plemyria rubiginata* Schiff. (Blue-bordered Carpet)

Widespread at varying density. This equally pretty small moth has been recorded lately in 20 localities all over the county. It seems to occur in most only at low density though it is fairly common in a few areas. The VCH stated that it was extremely scarce at Colchester and Langham, where it had formerly been common, but gave no other localities. However, we know that it was very common in Epping Forest in the 1880s (e.g. *Entomologist*, 16:153) and the

107

likelihood is that it was at least as widespread at the turn of the century as it is today.

*Chloroclysta siterata* Hufn. (Red-green Carpet)

Very local and scarce. This species has been found in recent years at both Lexden (Colchester) and Berechurch at ivy bloom in the autumn (JF) and occurs occasionally at Benfleet and Hadleigh, the last in 1969 (HCH). Single examples occurred at Bradwell-on-Sea on 24 May and 6 October 1960 (AJD). The VCH did not mention it.

*Chloroclysta miata* L. (Autumn Green Carpet)

Rare. The VCH described this other autumnal green carpet as of general occurrence, especially at gas lamps. It has since almost vanished from Essex as the only subsequent records come from Hadleigh where it is seen occasionally (HCH) and Westcliff-on-Sea where one occurred in October 1970 (HCH).

*Dysstroma truncata* Hufn. (Common Marbled Carpet)

Generally distributed and common.

*Dysstroma citrata* L. (Dark Marbled Carpet)

Local. The VCH regarded this moth as much less common than *D. truncata* (above) which it closely resembles. This is still the case: indeed, the present species seems largely to be confined to the west side of the county. There it is to be found regularly in Hatfield Forest (GHBS), single specimens occurred at Quendon in August 1959 (AME) and Debden in 1969 (GHBS), and there is an undated record from Epping Forest (*London Nat.*, 36:79). Elsewhere it has been noted occasionally at Hadleigh (HCH) and rarely at Colchester between 1956 and 1960 (JF).

*Thera obeliscata* Hübn. (Grey Pine Carpet)

Widespread and locally common. The VCH indicated that 'T. variata' was common among larch and Scotch fir: this must be regarded as a reference to the present species with which *T. variata* was then confused. It is still widely distributed, having been noted recently in 18 localities spread over much of the county, and it seems to be one of those species which is able to exist in districts where its host trees are few and far between. Most specimens seen nowadays are melanic.

*Thera variata* Schiff. (Grey Spruce Carpet)

This carpet, which was not recognised as a British insect until 1911, has only recently been added to the Essex list. Single examples of the nominate (continental) form were noted on Danbury Ridge in early September 1968 (CH, FBM) and on 27 October 1972 (GAP).

*Thera juniperata* L. (Juniper Carpet)

The VCH stated that this species was to be found at Donyland near Colchester, where it was not very common. The only subsequent records relate to several at Maldon in November 1935 (GAP), two on Danbury Ridge in late October 1972 (GAP), and one at Little Hallingbury in the west on 19 October 1973 (JLF). It is remarkable that *T. juniperata* should be found in Essex at all and it would be interesting to discover on what the larvae had fed.

*Hydriomena furcata* Thunb. (July Highflyer)

Generally distributed and common. The greenish, dark-banded form *sordidata* Fab. is predominant.

*Hydriomena coerulata* F. (May Highflyer)

Distinctly local. The VCH did not regard this moth as very common but said that it could usually be found among alder. Its status is not very different today: it is known to occur at low density in 12 localities, viz., Bradwell-on-Sea, rarely (AJD); Hadleigh (HCH); Danbury Ridge (GAP); around Brentwood at Thorndon Park (RRC), Ingrave (KWG) and Coxtie Green (PJW); Writtle (Writtle Ag. Coll. coll.); Stondon Massey and Ongar (DCT); Berechurch and Earls Colne (JF); and Dovercourt, rarely (MEA). There is an undated record from Epping Forest (*London Nat.*, 36:96). The colour of Essex specimens ranges from the typical whitish to the sooty black of the melanic ab. *obsoletaria* Schille.

*Philereme vetulata* Schiff. (Brown Scallop)

Very local and scarce. The VCH recorded this insect only from Epping and Saffron Walden but there is a further old record from Navestock. Two of the four subsequent reports also come from the west side of the county, viz., Hatfield Forest, July 1956 and 1962 (GHBS); Takeley, July 1972 (GHBS). It is common in a restricted locality at Bradwell-on-Sea where it was first recorded in 1956 and has apparently established itself on introduced *Rhamnus* (AJD), and is scarce on Danbury Ridge (GAP).

*Philereme transversata* Hufn. (Dark Umber)

Very local and scarce. As in the case of the last species, *P. transversata*, which is also known as the Dark Scallop, is recorded only from Epping and Saffron Walden by the VCH although Purleigh near Maldon and Navestock are also mentioned in the old literature. Subsequent records from west and north-west Essex are: Debden area, singly in 1935, 1937 and 1938 (PFA) and August 1969 (GHBS); Saffron Walden, 1–2 in most years (AME); Widdington, 1974 (GHBS). Elsewhere it occurs at low density on Danbury Ridge (GAP) and was recorded at Writtle in 1967 (Writtle Ag. Coll. coll.) and Bradwell-on-Sea in 1974 (AJD).

*Triphosa dubitata* L. (Common Tissue)

Very local and scarce. Once again the VCH gave Epping Forest and Saffron Walden as the localities in which this moth was known but one occurred at Shenfield in 1923 (EFW). The only later records come from Bradwell-on-Sea where it has occurred sparsely in nine years since 1954 (AJD, CD); Westcliff-on-Sea where odd specimens have occurred, the last in 1970 (HCH); and a locality south-west of Chelmsford where one was taken on 14 April 1973 (recorder's name withheld).

*Rheumaptera cervinalis* Scop. (Scarce Tissue)

Fairly widespread at low density. The VCH gave only Epping Forest, Saffron Walden and Colchester (occasionally) as localities for this species. It appears to have extended its range considerably and, despite its vernacular name, is now far and away the more prevalent of the two tissues, having been recorded sparingly or rarely in 16 localities covering all divisions of the county, in most of which it is a garden insect laying its eggs on ornamental *Berberis*.

*Rheumaptera undulata* L. (Scallop Shell)

Local and scarce. According to the VCH this beautiful species, although not common, was to be found in most woods. The position today is very different as the only recent records are: Bradwell-on-Sea, 1958, 1960 and 1963 (AJD); Hadleigh/Benfleet, local and scarce (HCH); Lexden (Colchester) and Donyland, single examples, July–August 1956–59 (JF); Elmstead Market, one, June 1974 (CNHS:JF); Mayland, one, August 1971 (PCF); Dovercourt/Ramsey/Wrabness, fairly regular at low density (MEA).

*Epirrhoe rivata* Hübn. (Wood Carpet)

Local and generally scarce. This fine carpet was described by the VCH as 'somewhat common locally'. Today it is probably more local and is certainly scarcer than at the beginning of the century, as it has been noted, at low density, in recent years only at Bradwell-on-Sea (AJD), Benfleet (HCH), Danbury Ridge where it is occasionally fairly common (GAP), Ingrave (KWG), Felsted (MFW) and Wickham Bishops (GCD).

*Epirrhoe alternata* Müll. (Common Carpet)

Also known as the Common Bedstraw Carpet, this species is generally distributed and common in a number of areas.

*Chesias legatella* Schiff. (The Streak)

Widely distributed. This and the next species are peculiarly narrow-winged geometers of similar appearance, yet readily distinguishable from one another. Their larvae feed on broom. The present species is on the wing in the autumn and its close relative in the spring and early summer. The VCH stated that it abounded among its food-plant and it is still fairly widespread and locally numerous, although it appears to be very local on the west side of the county.

*Chesias rufata* F. (Broom-tip)

Somewhat local. The VCH described it as 'very much scarcer' than *C. legatella* although it was probably also to be found in most places where broom grew freely. This fairly reflects its present status as it is rather more local than the last species and in most localities where both occur is usually the less numerous of the two. Like *C. legatella* it seems to be thinly spread in the west.

*Anaitis plagiata* L. (Slender Treble-Bar)

Widespread. Although it can no longer be claimed, as the VCH did, that this attractive, predominantly day-flying species is of general occurrence among its food-plant, *Hypericum* (St. John's-wort), it is still fairly widespread although its density is generally rather low and it is doubtfully numerous anywhere today.

*Anaitis efformata* Guen. (Short-clasped Treble Bar)
Apparently rare. This species, also known as the Lesser Treble-bar, was only recognised as a distinct species 50 years ago. It was not uncommon in a locality in the Rochford Hundred up to 1963 at least (HCH), but the only other Essex record concerns a single example on Danbury Ridge on 3 September 1973 (GAP). It may well have been overlooked in some districts as it is distinguished only with difficulty from *A. plagiata* from which it differs by its shorter body and more angulated innermost cross-line.

*Horisme vitalbata* Schiff. (Small Waved Umber)
Fairly widespread. As stated by the VCH this distinctive moth is generally to be found among *Clematis vitalba* (Traveller's Joy) and its distribution conforms closely with the food-plant's range. In recent years it has been recorded at varying density from 17 widely scattered localities, in a very few of which the food-plant does not occur: such cases may denote that the species has established itself here and there on garden *Clematis*.

*Horisme tersata* Schiff. (Fern)
Rather local; not common. The VCH bracketed this moth with *H. vitalbata* (above) in describing it as of general occurrence among *Clematis*. Today, however, it appears to be rather less widespread than the last species: noted of late in some 15 localities spread throughout the county it is decidedly scarce in most and nowhere numerous.

*Lobophora halterata* Hufn. (Large Seraphim)
Widespread in suitable areas. According to the VCH this geometer with its ample forewings was widely distributed at the turn of the century among poplars and aspens and this is still the case. Recorded in 15 localities covering all parts of the county it is, however, generally scarce and is currently reported as fairly numerous only on Danbury Ridge (DGD, GAP) and in Thorndon Park (PCF.)

*Mysticoptera sexalata* Retz. (Small Seraphim)
Extremely local. Formerly noted among sallow at Colchester, St. Osyth and near Maldon at Hazeleigh (VCH), at present this small moth is known to occur only on Danbury Ridge where it is fairly common locally (DGD, GAP).

*Acasis viretata* Hübn. (Yellow-barred Brindle)
Rather local. This yellowish-green species was recorded by the VCH only from Epping, Walthamstow and (once only) from Colchester. It is known to be markedly more widespread than that today but as it occurs only at low density in most of its haunts it may have escaped attention in the past. It seems to be most

prevalent in the Rochford Hundred and on Danbury Ridge (GAP) where it is fairly common in some years, and has also been noted recently on Thames-side and Langdon Hills (RT) and at Grays (RRC) in the south; further north at Ingrave (KWG), Coxtie Green (PJW) and Blackmore (RT); at Hatfield Forest (BSCNHS) and Takeley (GHBS) in the west; and at Dovercourt in the north-east (MEA).

*Trichopteryx carpinata* Borkh. (Early Tooth-striped)
Very local. It was plentiful in Epping Forest in 1894 (*Ent. Rec.*, 5: 69) but the VCH gave only Donyland and St. Osyth as localities for this spring species. It still occurs at Donyland as well as at Lexden and West Bergholt (JF). Its only other Essex stronghold is the Blackmore district south-west of Chelmsford, where it is fairly common (RRC, WLC, RT). Otherwise it has been noted only at Bradwell-on-Sea on 9 May 1967 (AJD), Benfleet and Hadleigh where 1–2 occurred annually up to 1969 at least (HCH), and in Hatfield Forest in 1948 (PBMA).

*Orthonoma lignata* Hübn. (Oblique Carpet)
Very local and scarce. West Bergholt and Rainham were the only localities given by the VCH for this small marsh-haunting species. More recently it has occurred at Bradwell-on-Sea in 10 years since 1947 (AJD), annually near Rochford where it may still be found (HCH), and at Westcliff-on-Sea (2) in July 1962 (HCH).

*Ortholitha plumbaria* F. (July Lead Belle)
Very local. The VCH stated that this day-flier was sometimes common in heathy places among furze. It is fairly common in a restricted locality in the interior of the county (recorder's name withheld) but the only other recent records relate to single examples taken at Ingrave on 2 July 1964 (KWG) and on Thames-side on 25 June 1966 and 4 July 1968 (RT).

*Ortholitha chenopodiata* L. (Shaded Broad-bar)
Generally distributed and common. Very numerous in open un-cultivated country, especially around the coast and estuaries.

*Ortholitha bipunctaria* Schiff. (Chalk Carpet)
Rare. The VCH gave Epping, Southend-on-Sea and Harwich as localities for this neat greyish moth and added that it had dis-appeared from Walton-on-the-Naze, where it had formerly occurred in some numbers, following sea encroachment. It is sur-prising that this species of chalk and limestone should, apparently, once have been established in north-east Essex. More recently what have probably been wanderers from Kent have appeared occasionally on Hadleigh Downs (HCH), while one was noted in Grays Chalk Quarry N.R. on 28 July 1968 (GAP).

*Larentia clavaria* Haw. (Mallow Carpet)
Widespread. 'Common among mallow and hollyhock' was the VCH's summary of the status of this species which closely re-

112

sembles *O. chenopodiata* (above) but is larger and appears in the autumn. Today it is still widely distributed but it generally occurs at rather low density away from the coast and estuaries, on parts of which it is quite numerous.

*Pelurga comitata* L. (Dark Spinach)
Fairly widely distributed. According to the VCH this species was 'sometimes plentiful among *Chenopodium*'. Today it can be described as fairly widespread, although not particularly numerous, both inland and along the coast and estuaries where its larva feeds on *Atriplex* (Orache) as well as Goosefoot.

*Oporinia dilutata* Schiff. (November Carpet)
Generally distributed and common. Very numerous in some well-wooded districts.

*Oporinia christyi* Prout (Pale November Carpet)
Apparently rare. This species, which is also known as Christy's Carpet, is distinguished from *O. dilutata* (above) only with difficulty and may, therefore, have been overlooked on occasion. It had not been separated from *O. dilutata* at the time the VCH was published and, since its recognition, has been reported with certainty only from Thundersley on 26 October 1962 (DGD) and Dovercourt on 22 and 28 October 1972 (MEA).

*Operophtera brumata* L. (Common Winter Moth)
Very common everywhere; abundant in some districts.

*Operophtera fagata* Scharf. (Northern Winter Moth)
Local. Epping, Harwich and St. Osyth were the only localities given in the VCH for this moth of birch woodland and the only subsequent records are: Bradwell-on-Sea, irregular, not common (AJD); Rochford Hundred, not uncommon locally (DGD, HCH); Danbury Ridge, generally common and locally abundant (GAP); Thrift Wood N.R., Bicknacre, December 1971 (GAP); Thorndon Park, several noted (RRC); Chigwell Row, common (IS). Although this species is noticeably larger and paler than *O. brumata* (above), it may well have been overlooked in other suitable localities: despite its vernacular name it is widespread in the southern half of England.

*Asthena albulata* Hufn. (Small White Wave)
Local. The VCH described this little moth, which is also known as the White Waved Carpet, as abundant everywhere. Even allowing for the possibility that it may to some extent have been overlooked it seems much less widespread today and mostly to be found in well-wooded districts. Recent records are: Bradwell-on-Sea, 1950–52 and 1958 only (AJD); Rochford Hundred, locally common (DGD, HCH); Langdon Hills, June 1968 (RT); Thorndon Park, locally common (RRC) but only one (June 1972) at nearby Ingrave (KWG); Blackmore, locally common (RRC, RT); Danbury Ridge, rather uncommon (GAP); Stondon Massey, June 1973 (DCT);

Quendon, 1959 and 1968 (AME); Donyland Woods and Friday Woods, Berechurch, locally common (JF).

*Minoa murinata* Scop. (Drab Looper)

Very rare; possibly extinct. The only localities given by the VCH for this small moth, which is sometimes called the Drab Carpet and is a day-flier, were the Southend-on-Sea district and St. Osyth. It has subsequently been found only at Benfleet where it was scarce in 1936 and again in 1948–49 but has not been seen since (HCH).

*Hydrelia flammeolaria* Hufn. (Small Yellow Wave)

Fairly widespread; not common. According to the VCH this attractive little moth, also called the Yellow Waved Carpet, was common among maple and, to a lesser extent, alder. It is still found in a number of localities but is nowhere common. It has been reported in recent years from Bradwell-on-Sea (AJD); parts of the Rochford Hundred (DGD, HCH); Thames-side and Grays Chalk Quarry N.R. (RT); Epping Forest (*Proc. S. Lond. ent. nat. Hist. Soc.*, 1947–8:64); Hookend (RRC); Coxtie Green (PJW); Danbury Ridge (GAP); Stondon Massey (DCT); Takeley (GHBS); Saffron Walden (AME); and on the north-east coast at Walton-on-the-Naze (JKW), Hamford Water (JBF) and Dovercourt (HEC).

*Euchoeca nebulata* Scop. (Dingy Shell)

Rather local and scarce. The VCH said that this species was rather common in the Colchester district and doubtless occurred generally among alder. There are no subsequent records from the Colchester area and it seems to be widely distributed only around Brentwood—Hall Wood, Brentwood (JF), Hookend and Thorndon Park (RRC) and Coxtie Green (PJW)—but it has also been noted recently at Hadleigh (HCH), Thames-side (RT), Danbury Ridge (GAP), Wickham Bishops (GCD), Stondon Massey (DCT), Saffron Walden (AME) and Dovercourt (MEA). It appears to be generally uncommon.


Forty-eight species of the large group of mostly diminutive moths comprising the genus *Eupithecia* and known collectively as 'pugs'—which rest with their comparatively slender wings at right angles to their bodies—have been recorded in the British Isles, and no fewer than 36 of them are known to have occurred in Essex during the past half-century. Few bear markings which readily distinguish them and the identification of the majority presents formidable problems to all but the few who have made a long and extensive study of the group. Consequently the distribution and density in Essex of the majority of the species are still imperfectly known and it would be surprising if a number had not been heavily under-recorded. This likelihood should be borne in mind when reference is made to the summaries of their apparent status which appear below.

*Eupithecia subumbrata* Schiff. (Shaded Pug)

Very local. The VCH recorded this predominantly coastal pug only from Southend-on-Sea, Shoeburyness and St. Osyth. It is still found in south-east Essex where it is locally common (HCH), is fairly common at Bradwell-on-Sea (AJD), and was taken on Thames-side in June 1967 and 1969 (RT) and at Dovercourt in 1974 (MEA). The only inland occurrences concern single specimens on Danbury Ridge in 1967 and 1974 (GAP).

*Eupithecia subnotata* Hübn. (Plain Pug)

Widespread. The VCH regarded this fairly large pug as common. Today, although not as addicted to the coast and its vicinity as the last species, it is nevertheless more numerous and widespread on the littoral than elsewhere. It is common in the Rochford Hundred (HCH) and has been noted in a number of other coastal and estuarine localities from Dovercourt round to East Tilbury. Inland it has occurred at Chelmsford and on Danbury Ridge (GAP) and at Lexden (JF), Coxtie Green (PJW) and Chigwell/Lambourne (IS).

*Eupithecia millefoliata* Rössl. (Yarrow Pug)

Very local. This fairly large greyish-white species, which is also known as the Milfoil Pug, was not added to the British list until the late 1940s. It was first taken in Essex at Westcliff-on-Sea on 5 August 1958 (HCH), a larva was found on *Achillea millefolium* (Yarrow) on Canvey Island in 1968 (AME), one was taken in Thorndon Park on 15 June 1973 (PCF), and it occurs almost annually in small numbers on Danbury Ridge (GAP).

*Eupithecia tenuiata* Hübn. (Slender Pug)

Local. Epping, Harwich, Southend-on-Sea and St. Osyth were given as localities for this small pug in the VCH. Currently it is common in the Rochford Hundred (HCH) and regular in small numbers on Danbury Ridge (GAP), while one was taken on Thames-side in May 1966 (RT). It may well prove to occur in most districts where sallow grows freely.

*Eupithecia inturbata* Hübn. (Maple Pug)

Local. Leigh-on-Sea is the only locality mentioned in the VCH but this tiny species is now known to occur in several localities. It is regular in small numbers on Danbury Ridge (GAP) and at Westcliff-on-Sea (HCH), and other recent records are: Saffron Walden, larvae, 1959 (AME); Little Chesterford, four, August 1960 (AME); Thames-side, August 1968 (RT); Quendon, well represented, July–August 1970 (AME); Grays Chalk Quarry N.R., July 1971 (RT); Doddinghurst, August 1973 (JTS).

*Eupithecia haworthiata* Doubl. (Haworth's Pug)

Apparently local. This equally diminutive pug was said by the VCH to 'abound among *Clematis*'. As much at home on cultivated *Clematis* as on the wild *C. vitalbata* it is surely much more widespread today than is suggested by the few records—which come from Bradwell-on-Sea (AJD), Westcliff-on-Sea (HCH), Thundersley (DGD), Danbury Ridge (GAP), Takeley (GHBS), Saffron Walden (AME) and Dovercourt (MEA).

*Eupithecia plumbeolata* Haw. (Lead-coloured Pug)

Local. Another very small insect, this species was stated by the VCH to be found in many woods among *Melampyrum pratense* (Common Cow-wheat). Lately it has been noted only at Bradwell-on-Sea where it is uncommon (AJD); in the Benfleet/Hadleigh/Thundersley area where it is locally common (DGD, HCH); on Danbury Ridge in June 1972 (GAP); in Thrift Wood, Bicknacre, N.R. in 1973 and 1974 (GAP), and at Thorndon Park in June 1973 (PCF).

*Eupithecia linariata* Schiff. (Toadflax Pug)

Widespread. This and the next species are richly-coloured moths resembling each other closely, but the former is smaller and more strongly marked than the latter. The VCH thought both would be found wherever their respective food-plants, *Linaria vulgaris* (Common Toadflax) and *Digitalis purpurea* (Foxglove), grew. *E. linariata* appears to be much the more widespread of the two today, having been noted at varying density in some 17 localities scattered over the county.

*Eupithecia pulchellata* Steph. (Foxglove Pug)

Local. This pug has been recorded of late, in woods or gardens where the food-plant grows, only from the Rochford Hundred (DGD, HCH), Ingrave (KWG), Langdon Hills (RT), Danbury Ridge (GAP, RT), Ongar (DCT), and Lexden and West Bergholt (JF). Here and there it is fairly numerous but generally its density appears to be lower than that of the last species with which, however, it can easily be confused.

*Eupithecia exiguata* Hübn. (Mottled Pug)

The VCH described this species as generally distributed and this is probably still the case although it has been noted only in a dozen or so localities, in most of which it is common or fairly so.

*Eupithecia insigniata* Hübn. (Pinion-spotted Pug)

Very rare. The VCH recorded it from Epping and Loughton and the only subsequent record is of one at Bradwell-on-Sea on 23 May 1950 (AJD).

*Eupithecia valerianata* Hübn. (Valerian Pug)

Rare. The VCH made no mention of this species but larvae were found on *Valeriana officinalis* (Common or Great Valerian) in the Chelmer Valley at Ulting near Maldon in July 1948 (HCH) and single specimens occurred at Thundersley on 29 July 1971 and 23 and 26 June 1972 (JC).

*Eupithecia venosata* F. (Netted Pug)

Rare. The VCH gave Braintree, Colchester and Danbury as

localities for this handsome pug and thought it would probably be found in most places where *Silene vulgaris* (Bladder Campion) grew. The only subsequent records are of one on 2 June 1967 (GAP) and two on 8 June 1973 (FBM, GAP) on Danbury Ridge. The food-plant is now very local in Essex.

*Eupithecia centaureata* Schiff. (Lime-speck Pug)
Generally distributed and common.

*Eupithecia trisignaria* H.-S. (Triple-spotted Pug)
Very local and scarce. The VCH stated that this insect had been noted only at Colchester where it was a great rarity. It has since been found only at Debden in the north-west where one was reared in 1968 from a larva on *Pimpinella major* (Greater Burnet-saxifrage) and others were seen on the same food-plant in August 1966 (AME); and at Bradwell-on-Sea where it is uncommon (AJD).

*Eupithecia intricata* Zett. (Edinburgh Pug)
subsp. *arceuthata* Freyer (Freyer's Pug)
Very local and scarce but probably increasing. *E. intricata* is represented in southern England by the large race *arceuthata* known as Freyer's Pug. In recent years it has extended its range and has been taken in Essex on nine occasions, viz., Westcliff-on-Sea, 5 August 1955 and 6 August 1966 (HCH); Hockley, 6 July 1956 (DGD); Bradwell-on-Sea, 30 June 1957, 3 June 1964 and 16 June 1969 (AJD); Danbury Ridge, 24 June 1971 (GAP); Ingrave, 16 and 18 June 1973 (KWG). It seems to be largely a garden species, the larvae feeding on various ornamental conifers, and may well appear in other districts.

*Eupithecia satyrata* Hübn. (Satyr Pug)
Very rare. Recorded by the VCH from the Harwich district, this species has since been taken only at Debden in north-west Essex on 9 June 1967 (AME).

*Eupithecia tripunctaria* H.-S. (White-spotted Pug)
Distinctly local. According to the VCH this pug had formerly been common but was then scarce. Of late years it has been found at varying density in 10 localities: none is further west than Brentwood but it may well await discovery in other parts of the county. Melanic examples are not rare.

*Eupithecia absinthiata* Clerck (Wormwood Pug)
Widely if not generally distributed and common in a number of districts.

*Eupithecia goossensiata* Mab. (Ling Pug)
Rare. This species is regarded in some quarters as a form of *E. absinthiata* which is associated with *Erica* and *Calluna* (heath and ling) although the larva is fairly distinct. The VCH recorded it only from Epping and Dedham but expected that it would be found generally where its food-plants grew. But there are only two sub-sequent records—of single specimens on Danbury Ridge on 10

117

August 1971 (GAP) and at Thorndon Park on 9 June 1973 (PCF).

*Eupithecia expallidata* Doubl. (Bleached Pug)
Very local and scarce. Not recorded by the VCH, this large shiny pug has since occurred only at Hadleigh where a few larvae were found regularly on *Solidago virgaurea* (Golden-rod) up to 1939 (HCH) and at Bradwell-on-Sea where it is uncommon (AJD).

*Eupithecia assimilata* Doubl. (Currant Pug)
Local. This species was said by the VCH to be 'sometimes common among currant and hop'. More recently it has been found sparingly at Bradwell-on-Sea (AJD) and not uncommonly in the Rochford Hundred (HCH) and at Lexden, Colchester (JF), while several have appeared in some years at Dovercourt (MEA) and odd specimens have been noted on Thames-side (RT) and Danbury Ridge (GAP) and at Saffron Walden (AME). Like other currant feeders it may have declined along with vegetable and market gardens and allotments but equally it may be overlooked as it is difficult to distinguish from smaller examples of *E. absinthiata* (above).

*Eupithecia vulgata* Haw. (Common Pug)
Widely, perhaps generally, distributed and common in a number of districts. Melanic specimens are not infrequent.

*Eupithecia castigata* Hübn. (Grey Pug)
Widespread; common over much of its known range. Also prone to melanism.

*Eupithecia icterata* Vill. (Tawny Speckled Pug)
Very widely distributed and often common. The form occurring in Essex is the distinctive reddish *subfulvata* Haw.

*Eupithecia succenturiata* L. (Bordered Pug)
Widespread. The VCH gave as localities for this species only the Colchester, Maldon and Harwich districts but it is now known to enjoy a wide distribution having been noted in 16 localities, in some of which it is fairly common. As it is unlikely that this quite large whitish pug was overlooked to this extent in earlier times it may well have extended its range in recent years.

*Eupithecia indigata* Hübn. (Ochreous Pug)
Very local. The VCH made no reference to this pine and larch feeder but larvae were found at Feering Bury, Kelvedon, in July 1921 (*Entomologist*, 54:245). It has been noted since only at Lexden, Colchester, where it occurs regularly (JF), and on Danbury Ridge where one was taken on 23 May 1970 (GAP).

*Eupithecia pimpinellata* Hübn. (Pimpinel Pug)
Rare. The VCH stated that this pug was sometimes common, especially on the boulder clay, among *Pimpinella saxifraga* (Burnet-saxifrage). The only subsequent record relates to a number of larvae on the food-plant at Saffron Walden in 1959 (AME).

*Eupithecia extensaria* Freyer (Scarce Pug)

Rare. Two examples of this extremely local British pug were found in a coastal locality in July 1961 and six specimens were reared from the ova obtained (JF).

*Eupithecia nanata* Hübn. (Narrow-winged Pug)

Very local and scarce. The VCH recorded this distinctively shaped species only from Crockleford near Colchester but felt that it would probably be found in most areas containing heather. Subsequent records are: Leigh-on-Sea, formerly not uncommon among heather but localities largely destroyed by building (HCH); Bradwell-on-Sea, odd examples from time to time (AJD); Thames-side, one, May 1966 (RT); Danbury Ridge, two, September 1972 (GAP); Hamford Water, one, 1973 (JBF). Records from 'heatherless' districts may refer to wanderers although equally it may have established itself here and there on garden varieties of the food-plant.

(*Eupithecia innotata* Hufn. (Angle-barred Pug)

Specimens assigned to this species have been taken over the years at Shoeburyness, Lexden (Colchester) and Bradwell-on-Sea (2). It is now regarded as doubtful whether *E. innotata* has occurred in the British Isles and until the position is clear it is felt best to place supposed records of this species within brackets.)

*Eupithecia fraxinata* Crewe (Ash Pug)

Rare. The VCH stated that it occurred sparingly at Colchester. More recently it has been recorded only from Westcliff-on-Sea where it was first noted in June 1954 and 1–2 have since occurred from time to time (HCH).

*Eupithecia virgaureata* Doubl. (Golden-rod Pug)

Rare. Epping was the only locality given for this species in the VCH. It has since been found only at Hadleigh where a few larvae were found regularly on *Solidago virgaurea* (Golden-rod) up to 1939 (HCH), and Lexden (Colchester) where a few occurred annually in the late 1950s and early 1960s (JF).

*Eupithecia abbreviata* Steph. (Brindled Pug)

Widely distributed and probably to be found wherever oak grows freely. Melanic examples have occurred from time to time in south-east Essex (HCH).

*Eupithecia dodoneata* Guen. (Oak-tree Pug)

Very local. The VCH mentioned Epping, Loughton and Harwich as localities for this little moth and added that it was far from common elsewhere. In east Essex it is fairly common at Bradwell-on-Sea (AJD), in the south-east a few were noted at Hadleigh from 1935–39 (HCH) and three at Thundersley in May 1972 (JC), while on the north-east coast 1–2 occurred at Dovercourt in 1970 and 1972 (MEA) and one at Hamford Water in the latter year (JBF). *Quercus ilex*, the Holm or Evergreen Oak, a favourite host tree, is widespread on the Essex littoral. Further inland, larvae were found on oak at Warley, Brentwood, in June 1953 (*Proc. S. Lond. ent. nat. Hist. Soc.*, 1933–4:15) and single imagines at Debden in June 1969 (AME) and on Danbury Ridge in May 1970 (GAP).

*Eupithecia sobrinata* Hübn. (Juniper Pug)

Very local. The VCH indicated that it was not uncommon at Donyland and had occurred at Woodford. One taken at Westcliff-on-Sea in June 1955 was assumed to have been imported on ornamental juniper (HCH) while another at Saffron Walden in July 1970 was suspected of having been bred on such a shrub in the recorder's garden (AME). However, it has been common at least since 1969 (with a melanic example in 1974) in a restricted locality on Danbury Ridge where no juniper is present in the immediate vicinity although there is a variety of other evergreen trees and shrubs (GAP).

*Eupithecia lariciata* Freyer (Larch Pug)

Very rare. The VCH stated that this species was not uncommon among larch in the Colchester district and it is recorded from Epping Forest in 1893 (*Ent. Rec.*, 5:21). The only later records that can be traced are from Theydon Bois in 1912 (*London Nat.*, 37:141) and Canfield Hart Wood near Takeley where a larva (from which an imago was bred) was found in June 1944 (CC). It may be overlooked on occasion as it closely resembles some examples of the common *E. castigata* (above).

*Chloroclystis coronata* Hübn. (V Pug)

Widespread. It is surprising that the VCH said of this conspicuous though small green insect with its black 'v' mark on the forewings only that it 'sometimes occurs freely about Colchester, especially on the boulder clay', as it has been noted in recent years from 15 widely-scattered localities, in a number of which it is common.

*Chloroclystis rectangulata* L. (Green Pug)

Generally distributed and common in a number of districts. The vast majority of specimens today are melanic.

*Chloroclystis chloërata* Mabille (Sloe Pug)

This pug, which so closely resembles *C. rectangulata* in the imaginal stage that it was overlooked as a British species until 1971 (*Ent. Rec.*, 84:205), was first recorded in Essex in 1972 when larvae were discovered on blackthorn at Elmdon in the north-west on 26 April (DJLA). Two larvae were found on Danbury Ridge on 21 April 1974 (RRC) and two imagines in the same district in July 1974 (GAP). It may well prove to be widely distributed in the county.

*Gymnoscelis pumilata* Hübn. (Double-striped Pug)

Widely, perhaps generally, distributed and locally common.

*Abraxas sylvata* Scop. (Clouded Magpie)

Very local. The VCH gave Laindon and Epping Forest as localities for this handsome moth. It is still quite common in the restricted locality near Laindon to which the VCH refers (RT *et al.*) and has also been recorded during the past 50 years as follows: Colchester, several, 1947 (W. P. Seabrook coll.); Bradwell, very small numbers in six years since 1951 (AJD); Danbury Ridge, one, June 1967 (GAP); Dovercourt, one, July 1967 (MEA); Hadleigh, two, singly, in different localities, 1969 (*per* HCH); Wrabness, two, July 1972 (MEA).

*Abraxas grossulariata* L. (Magpie)

Generally distributed and common but on the whole much less numerous than formerly when, according to the VCH, it sometimes abounded among currant and gooseberry bushes and around blackthorn. A most variable species, a large number of aberrations, some quite remarkable, have been described.

*Lomaspilis marginata* L. (Clouded Border)

This variable species is very widely distributed and common in many districts.

*Ligdia adustata* Schiff. (Scorched Carpet)

Rather widely distributed; not common. The VCH described this attractive little moth, which is also called the Scorched Silver, as common everywhere. Today, though fairly widespread, it is by no means generally distributed and is doubtfully numerous anywhere. Reported from 18 localities it is probably to be found in most places where its food-plant, spindle, still grows.

*Bapta distinctata* H.-S. (Sloe Carpet)

Fairly common locally. As the larva feeds on blackthorn, Sloe Carpet seems a more apt vernacular name than the alternative 'Carpet Thorn' for this small, greyish-brown moth which is confined to south-east England where it occurs locally from Hampshire to Suffolk. It is probably as widespread and common in Essex as in any county. The only locality mentioned in the VCH is Colchester but the literature shows that it was known to occur in a number of other places by the turn of the century. Although there are several old records for Epping Forest and district and it is found just over the county boundary in Cambridgeshire, it has not been noted in recent years anywhere on the west side of the county. However, east of a line running through Brentwood northeastwards to Writtle and thence through West Bergholt near Colchester it is widespread, having been reported from 20 localities, in a number of which it is quite common.

*Bapta bimaculata* F. (White-pinion Spotted)

Local. According to the VCH this delicate little white species had only been reported from Epping Forest. Today its range, like that of *B. distinctata* (above), is largely confined to the east side of the county, but it is not nearly as widely distributed as the last species. There are no further records from Epping Forest and otherwise it has been noted in west Essex only at Wallbury Dells, Little

Hallingbury, in 1944 (CC). In the eastern half of the county it is not uncommon locally in the Rochford Hundred (HCH); occurred on 23 May 1972 at Bradwell-on-Sea (AJD); appears regularly at Berechurch, Donyland and Wrabness (JF); and was noted in 1971–72 at Dovercourt (MEA). It is also recorded from Wickham Bishops (GCD) and Great Maplestead (BWJP).

*Bapta temerata* Schiff. (Clouded Silver)
Very widely distributed and common in a number of districts.

*Deilinia pusaria* L. (Common White Wave)
Generally distributed and common in many areas.

*Deilinia exanthemata* Scop. (Common Wave)
Widely, perhaps generally, distributed and locally numerous.

*Ellopia fasciaria* L. (Barred Red)
Local and scarce. The VCH stated that this moth was found at Birch, Colchester and near Harwich. It is still most frequently met with in north-east Essex as it is found regularly on the outskirts of Colchester at Lexden, Old Heath and Berechurch (JF) and was noted at Dovercourt in July 1967 (MEA) and Aldham in July 1971 (MRSM). Recent occurrences much further south and west, at Shenfield (MT) and Dunmow (MLT) in 1972 and Stondon Massey in 1973 (DCT), all in July, suggest that the species may possibly be in the process of extending its range.

*Campaea margaritata* L. (Light Emerald)
Widespread. This delicate pale green species, now sometimes known as the Barred Light Green to distinguish it from the true 'emeralds', is widely distributed and is very common in some well-wooded districts.

*Angerona prunaria* L. (Orange Moth)
Widespread; not very common. According to the VCH this colourful moth was to be found frequently in many woods. It has almost certainly decreased markedly since then: such a conspicuous species as this can hardly have been overlooked, yet although it has been reported in recent years from some 20 localities it seems to occur only at low density in most of them, and there are several extensively wooded areas, e.g., the Brentwood district, in which it has not been noted of late.

*Semiothisa notata* L. (Blunt-angled Peacock)
Local and uncommon. The status of this attractive moth has changed little since the VCH described it as scarce and local and gave three areas in north-east Essex, Brentwood and Southend-on-Sea as localities. The only subsequent records are: Bradwell-on-Sea, fairly regular in small numbers but less prevalent than *S. alternaria* below (AJD); Hadleigh, very small numbers up to 1939 when last searched for (HCH); Thundersley, scarce (DGD); Westcliff-on-Sea, singly, June 1956 and June 1961 (HCH); West Bergholt, one, June 1956 (JF); Danbury Ridge, one in July 1964 (JF) and two

122

in June 1970 (GAP, RT); Dovercourt, two in August 1969 and one in August 1971 (MEA); Thames-side, one, June 1970 (RT); Hornchurch, two, 1973 (WLC).

*Semiothisa alternaria* Hübn. (Sharp-angled Peacock)
Extremely local. No reference is made to this species in the VCH but it occurs fairly regularly in small numbers at Bradwell-on-Sea where it appears to be more prevalent than *S. notata* above (AJD). The only other record is of one at Hamford Water in 1970 (JBF).

*Semiothisa signaria* Hübn.
The first British specimen of this continental species, which resembles the next but lacks its tawny colouration, was taken in the interior of the county on 20 June 1970 (RT; *Ent. Rec.*, 86:195, with photograph).

*Semiothisa liturata* Clerck (Tawny-barred Angle)
Somewhat local. The VCH stated that this species was 'somewhat common at Langham and Colchester before the larches on which it fed were cut down'. Presumably Harwood knew of no other records and this is borne out by the literature. At present it is known to occur in about a dozen localities with strongholds around Colchester (JF), south of Brentwood (RRC, KWG *et al.*) and on Danbury Ridge (GAP). Otherwise it has been noted, generally either at very low density or as odd specimens, at Bradwell-on-Sea (AJD), Thundersley (DGD), Langdon Hills (RT), Coxtie Green (PJW), Ongar (DCT), Debden (AME), Great Maplestead (BWJP) and Dovercourt (MEA). The melanic ab. *nigrofulvata* Collins is not rare.

*Theria rupicapraria* Schiff. (Early Moth)
Generally distributed and common.

*Erannis leucophaearia* Schiff. (Spring Usher)
Quite widespread. The VCH described this pretty little moth of the late winter as common. It is by no means universally so today, although it is still fairly widespread at varying density. The 15 widely-scattered localities in which it has been noted of late include Epping Forest (HEC) and Ongar (DCT) but it has not occurred elsewhere on the west side of the county. The melanic ab. *merularia* Weymer is becoming prevalent.

*Erannis aurantiaria* Hübn. (Scarce Umber)
Very widely distributed and, despite its vernacular name, more numerous than *E. defoliaria* (below) in some well-wooded districts.

*Erannis marginaria* F. (Dotted Border)
Generally distributed and common.

*Erannis defoliaria* Clerck (Mottled Umber)
Very widely distributed and common in many districts, continuing on the wing well into the winter. An exceedingly variable species, it shows a marked tendency to melanism in some areas, particularly in the Epping Forest district (see, e.g., *London Nat.*, 37:157).

*Anagoga pulveraria* L. (Barred Umber)

Very local and scarce. Seemingly this species has declined considerably during this century as the VCH stated that it was to be found frequently in woods whereas today it appears to be confined to certain areas in the south-east and north-east. In the former a total of four was noted at Hadleigh in 1937–38 (HCH) and it is scarce at Thundersley (DGD); while in the latter it is reported at low density from Lexden (Colchester), West Bergholt, Great Horkesley and Earls Colne (JF).

*Ennomos autumnaria* Wernb. (Large Thorn)

Widespread. This fine moth was known to occur only in extreme south-east England during the nineteenth century but it has since extended its range considerably and is now widespread in all the seaboard counties from Hampshire to Suffolk and is spreading even further afield. The VCH knew only of single specimens at Shoeburyness and Harwich but it now enjoys a wide if still patchy distribution in the county. Recorded from some 20 localities its density varies widely from place to place although it is generally more numerous in the east and has yet to be noted in some quite extensive areas in the centre and north.

*Ennomos quercinaria* Hufn. (August Thorn)

Local. The VCH stated that this thorn was to be found in many oak woods and was much less scarce than *D. erosaria* (below). At present it is distinctly local and less widespread than the last-mentioned species. Localities from which it has been reported in recent years, mostly at low density or only occasionally, are: Bradwell-on-Sea (AJD); Westcliff-on-Sea (HCH), Thundersley (DGD) and Benfleet (JEC) in south-east Essex; Thames-side (RT); Hookend (RRC); Epping Forest (HEC); near Colchester at Lexden, Old Heath, Berechurch and Donyland (JF); Lamarsh in the north (FDB: CNHS); and Dovercourt in the extreme north-east (MEA).

*Deuteronomos alniaria* L. (Canary-shouldered Thorn)

Very widely distributed and quite numerous in a number of localities.

*Deuteronomos fuscantaria* Steph. (Dusky Thorn)

Widespread and fairly common in some districts: it is probably to be found wherever ash grows freely.

*Deuteronomos erosaria* Schiff. (September Thorn)

Fairly widespread. As stated under *E. quercinaria* (above), *D. erosaria* appears to be distinctly more widespread than that species although the VCH suggested that the reverse was the case at the turn of the century. Reported from some 16 widely-scattered localities its density appears to be on the low side over most of its range.

*Selenia bilunaria* Esp. (Early Thorn)

Generally distributed and common.

*Selenia lunaria* Schiff. (Lunar Thorn)

Widespread at low density. The VCH stated that this attractive thorn was nowhere common but was to be found in many places. This aptly sums up its present-day status: reported from over 20 localities covering all divisions of the county except the north-west, it is not numerous anywhere and scarce or very scarce over much of its range.

*Selenia tetralunaria* Hufn. (Purple Thorn)

Very widespread; not common. The VCH described this handsome thorn as extremely local and gave as localities only Epping, Hainault and Harwich. It has since extended its range very considerably as it has been noted in 25 localities spread all over the county except the north-west. Nowhere numerous, it occurs at distinctly low density over much of its range.

*Apeira syringaria* L. (Lilac Beauty)

Widely distributed but not common, as was the case in the VCH's day. This beautiful moth is rather less widespread than *S. tetralunaria* (above) and in most areas its density appears to be even lower than that of the last species. However, it has increased noticeably during the last few years at Bradwell-on-Sea (AJD), Ongar and Stondon Massey (DCT) and on Danbury Ridge (GAP), and it remains to be seen whether this trend becomes general.

*Gonodontis bidentata* Clerck (Scalloped Hazel)

Very widely, perhaps generally, distributed and common or fairly so in many localities.

*Colotois pennaria* L. (Feathered Thorn)

Equally as well distributed and common as the last species.

*Crocallis elinguaria* L. (Scalloped Oak)

Another almost generally distributed and common species.

*Plagodis dolabraria* L. (Scorched Wing)

Fairly widespread. The VCH described this predominantly woodland species as widely distributed but not common. Its status has not changed a great deal: reported from 17 localities at varying density it is numerous in some of the more extensively wooded areas.

*Opisthograptis luteolata* L. (Brimstone Moth)

This well-known yellow species, alternatively known as the Sulphur Thorn, is common everywhere and is on the wing almost continuously from late April through to the autumn.

*Epione repandaria* Hufn. (Common Bordered Beauty)

Very widespread. The statement in the VCH that this attractive insect was widespread but not common is true today. Noted of late in no fewer than 26 localities it is generally quite scarce although it is fairly common in a few areas where sallow abounds.

*Pseudopanthera macularia* L. (Speckled Yellow)

This pretty little day-flier occurs in most woodlands of any size throughout the county and is quite common in some districts.

*Ourapteryx sambucaria* L. (Swallow-tailed Moth)

This large and familiar pale yellow species is generally distributed and is common in many localities.

*Phigalia pedaria* F. (Pale Brindled Beauty)

Widespread. This is the first species to emerge in the new year and in mild weather can be found early in January. It is reported from most parts of the county and is common in some districts. The melanic ab. *monacharia* Staud. is now quite prevalent, forming about 25 per cent of the examples occurring in south-east Essex (DGD, HCH).

*Apocheima hispidaria* Schiff. (Small Brindled Beauty)

Local. The VCH described this species as local and scarce and its status is still much the same. It is, however, fairly common locally at Hockley (RRC), Langdon Hills (RT), South Weald Park (RRC) and on Danbury Ridge (GAP). At Ongar and Stondon Massey, where it was formerly rare, it is now regular in small numbers (DCT). It is also reported from Bradwell-on-Sea (AJD), Hadleigh (HCH), Thundersley (DGD), Ingrave/Thorndon Park (PCF, KWG), Coxtie Green (PJW) and, in the extreme north-east, from Hamford Water (JBF).

*Lycia hirtaria* Clerck (Brindled Beauty)

Widely distributed and common in many districts. This well-known species is prevalent in towns as well as in rural areas and in Essex, as elsewhere, is to be found in parks and large gardens in urban areas including the Metropolis, in parts of which it is common. Several examples of ab. *nigra* Cockayne occur annually on Thames-side (RT).

*Biston strataria* Hufn. (Oak Beauty)

This handsome species of the early spring is very widespread in the county and is common in a number of well-timbered districts.

*Biston betularia* L. (Peppered Moth)

Generally distributed and common in many districts. The VCH stated that the melanic ab. *carbonaria* Jordan and intermediate forms were occasionally captured or bred. Today only a very small proportion of specimens is typical: at Ingrave 92 per cent of 150 examined in 1967 were *carbonaria* (KWG) while in the Rochford Hundred (HCH) and on Danbury Ridge (GAP) more than 90 per cent are now either ab. *carbonaria*, which predominates, or the intermediate ab. *insularia* Th.-Meig.

*Menophra abruptaria* Thunb. (Waved Umber)

Widespread. This handsome species is widely distributed at varying density but is common in only a few localities. The melanic ab. *fuscata* Tutt forms some 10 per cent of examples occurring in the Rochford Hundred (HCH).

*Cleora rhomboidaria* Schiff. (Willow Beauty)
Generally distributed and common.

*Cleorodes lichenaria* Hufn. (Brussels Lace)
Very rare; not recorded in the past decade. The VCH merely stated that it had formerly been common in the Colchester district but that it had recently disappeared. There is also an old (1882) record from Hazeleigh Wood. More recently it has occurred only in south-east Essex: there it appeared at Hadleigh occasionally up to 1939 and again in July 1958 (HCH) and at Westcliff-on-Sea in July 1960 (HCH).

*Alcis repondata* L. (Mottled Beauty)
Generally distributed and common.

*Boarmia roboraria* Schiff. (Great Oak Beauty)
Very local and scarce; not recorded during the past decade. The VCH stated that this fine moth occurred at Hainault, Warley and St. Osyth and had also been taken once at Colchester and formerly at Langham. More recently it has been noted only in west, south-west and south-east Essex. Russell James, writing in 1929 (*Entomologist*, 63:42), stated that a 'fine melanic race' formerly occurred in numbers in Ongar Park Wood, while it was recorded from Epping *c*. 1932 (*Proc. S. Lond. ent. nat. Hist. Soc.*, 1932–3:116) and 25–30 examples of the above-mentioned dark form in Epping Forest in 1937 (*Entomologist*, 71:27). In the Rochford Hundred it was scarce up to 1939 at Hadleigh (HCH) and a single example occurred at Thundersley in 1948 (DGD). The alleged occurrence of one at Hockley in 1956 (*Essex Nat.*, 30:69) was wrongly ascribed to DGD and cannot be traced.

*Pseudoboarmia punctinalis* Scop. (Pale Oak Beauty)
Widespread. In vivid contrast to *B. roboraria* (above) it would seem that this species has extended its range considerably during the present century as the VCH recorded it only from Hainault and St. Osyth whereas it is now to be found in wooded districts over most of the county and here and there in less well-timbered areas. Its density varies from district to district but it does not appear to be numerous anywhere. A good proportion of specimens show melanic tendencies.

*Ectropis biundularia* Borkh. (Early Engrailed)
Much confusion exists concerning the separation of this species from the next. Structurally there is no difference between them and in appearance they are virtually identical. They are, however, on the wing at different times and by this means they can be distinguished with relative safety. The present species flies from late March to early May according to season, again in July and early August, and not infrequently yet again in September and early October. *E. crepuscularia*, on the other hand, is single-brooded and is on the wing between mid-May and mid-June. The two species

had not been separated when the VCH was published but collectively they show a considerable extension of range this century as the VCH gave only Epping, Harwich and Colchester (once) as localities.

*E. biundularia* is widespread, especially in well-timbered areas, and has been noted in some 20 localities scattered throughout the county. It varies in density but is common in some extensively wooded districts.

*Ectropis crepuscularia* Schiff. (Small Engrailed)
Apparently very local. The following are the only records regarded as authentic by virtue of their dates: Hadleigh, present in small numbers up to 1965 at least (HCH); Danbury Ridge, one in late May *c*. 1965 (HCH); Lexden and Berechurch, common in June (JF); Earls Colne, several, 3 June 1971 (FDB: CNHS); Dovercourt, 1–2 in late May/June in some years (MEA).

*Ectropis consonaria* Hübn. (Square-spot)
Rare. The VCH recorded this species from Epping and it was noted there as recently as 20 May 1956 (HEC). The only other report concerns 1–2 annually at Hadleigh up to 1966 (HCH).

*Ectropis extersaria* Hübn. (Brindled White-spot)
Local. The VCH stated that this species was uncommon but enjoyed an extensive range, probably occurring in all large woods. Today it appears to be absent throughout the northern half of the county but it is fairly widespread in well-wooded districts elsewhere, although common or fairly so only in Ongar Park Wood (*Entomologist*, 71:27) and on Danbury Ridge (GAP). Elsewhere it has been noted at Benfleet (HCH), Hadleigh (HCH) and Thundersley (JC) in the south-east, Brentwood (*Proc. S. Lond. ent. nat. Hist. Soc.*, 1947–8:63), Thorndon Park (PCF), Epping Forest (*Entomologist*, 71:27), Blackmore (RT) and Wickham Bishops (GCD).

*Aethalura punctulata* Schiff. (Grey Birch)
Very widespread, being found in localities where birch grows throughout the county. In some of the more extensive birch woodlands it is very numerous.

*Gnophos obscurata* Schiff. (Common Annulet)
One, obviously a wanderer, at Boreham in August 1928 (W. P. Seabrook coll.) is the only Essex record.

*Ematurga atomaria* L. (Common Heath)
Formerly local, now rare. The VCH reported this small day-flying species from Layer-de-la-Haye and Stanford-le-Hope and added that it was probably to be found where any extent of heather remained: in fact it is recorded elsewhere in the old literature from Epping Forest and Danbury Ridge in the 1880s. It was found commonly in the Brentwood district and at Epping in 1942 (EFW) and not uncommonly at Hadleigh up to 1951 since when its locality has largely been destroyed (HCH).

*Bupalus piniaria* L. (Bordered White)
Local and scarce. The VCH gave Alresford, Birch and Brentwood as localities for this distinctive pine feeder. More recently it has been noted in 1957, 1959 and 1960 at Bradwell-on-Sea (AJD); occasionally in the Southend-on-Sea area (HCH) and at Ongar and Stondon Massey (DCT); singly at Thorndon Park/Ingrave in May 1940 (EFW), June 1970 (RRC) and June 1974 (KWG); at Old Heath, Colchester, in June 1956 and 1957 (JF); at Writtle in 1967 (Writtle Ag. Coll. coll.); in June 1970 at Doddinghurst (JTS) and on Danbury Ridge (GAP, RT); and in Honeywood Forest, Coggeshall (*c*. 6) in June 1974 (JF: CNHS). It may, therefore, be increasing.

*Itame wauaria* L. (V Moth)
Widespread; generally less common than formerly. The VCH stated that this currant-feeding, predominantly garden insect was moderately common. Today, although widely distributed, it is scarce or even rare in a number of districts but still common in a few.

*Itame brunneata* Thunb. (Rannoch Looper)
Rare vagrant. Four examples of this species which, in Great Britain, is resident only in the Scottish Highlands, have occurred in recent years, viz., Bradwell-on-Sea, 13 and 27 July 1955 and 26 June 1960 (AJD); Thames-side, 18 July 1968 (RT). Doubtless they were continental immigrants.

*Lithina chlorosata* Scop. (Brown Silver-lines)
Widespread, occurring in most places where bracken is well represented and approaching abundance in some extensive bracken-covered areas.

*Chiasmia clathrata* L. (Latticed Heath)
Very widely, if not generally, distributed and quite common in a number of localities.

*Aspitates ochrearia* Rossi (Yellow Belle)
Local. According to the VCH this species was common on the coast in the northern part of the county but it is now known to occur in most parts of the littoral, penetrating up the Thames as far as Mucking (RT), and is still common in some localities. Predominantly a seaboard species in Essex it is nevertheless locally common around Colchester at Berechurch, Donyland, Copford and Layer-de-la-Haye (JF), while it has also occurred, singly, at Wickham Bishops in 1971 (GCD) and in four years since 1966 at Thorndon Park/Ingrave (PCF, KWG). By far the furthest penetration inland, however, is of one at Great Maplestead in the north on 21 August 1960 (BWJP).

# Appendix

## Systematic list of species recorded in Essex prior to 1925 but not since.

Note: For the sake of brevity, where the VCH provides one of two or more references to an occurrence only the VCH is cited, except where another reference describes the event in greater detail when the latter is given instead of the VCH.

## *Rhopalocera* (Butterflies)

[*Parnassius apollo* L. (Apollo)
  An example of this alpine species taken at Epping in 1847 or 1848 (*Entomologist*, 6:39; *Ent. Rec.*, 71:276) must surely have been released.]

*Aporia crataegi* L. (Black-veined White)
  Epping Forest, 1850s (*London Nat.*, 29:76); at least one at Wanstead Flats in or prior to 1879 (*Entomologist*, 12:163).

*Leptidea sinapis* L. (Wood White)
  Plentiful in the Epping area until the mid-1800s; Ongar Park Woods, 1888; Debden (*Essex Nat.*, 5:83); near Colchester (i.e. Wrabness, St. Osyth, Bromley and Donyland Heath) and once at Coggeshall (VCH).

*Argynnis lathonia* L. (Queen of Spain Fritillary)
  As a rare immigrant, at Colchester (several), Braintree, Southend-on-Sea, Rainham and, in 1881, at St. Osyth (VCH); Colchester, two, 1918 (*Entomologist*, 52:48).

(*Clossiana dia* L. (Weaver's Fritillary)
  An example of this small continental fritillary was alleged to have been taken at Epping some years before 1883 (*Entomologist*, 16: 112).)

*Euphydryas aurinia* Rott. (Marsh Fritillary)
  Several localities around Epping, last seen 1872 (VCH); Ongar Park Wood, 1839 (*Essex Nat.*, 1:110).

*Hamearis lucina* L. (Duke of Burgundy)
  Tendring Hundred, Woodham Ferrers, Eastwood (VCH): Gaynes Park and Ongar Park Woods, mid-1800s (*Essex Nat.*, 5:106); Danbury, 1896 (*Essex Nat.*, 9:261); near Harwich, 1911 (*Entomologist*, 45:153); abundant near Rochford, 1924 (*Entomologist*, 57: 186).

*Thecla betulae* L. (Brown Hairstreak)
  Epping Forest, common in some seasons; Hazeleigh and Mundon;
  formerly at High Woods (Colchester) and Langham (VCH).
*Lysandra bellargus* Rott. (Adonis Blue)
  Taken once or twice near Saffron Walden (VCH).
*Cyaniris semiargus* Rott. (Mazarine Blue)
  Formerly taken near Saffron Walden (VCH).
*Cupido minimus* Fuessl. (Small Blue)
  Epping district; one near Saffron Walden (VCH).
*Hesperia comma* L. (Silver-spotted Skipper)
  (Danbury, 1884); Saffron Walden district (VCH).


# *Heterocera* (Moths)

*Celerio euphorbiae* L. (Spurge Hawk)
  Several larvae of this very rare immigrant were found at Harwich
  in June 1872 (*Entomologist*, 7:46).
*Hemaris tityus* L. (Narrow-bordered Bee Hawk)
  Epping Forest district; Colchester, 1896 (VCH)
*Harpyia bicuspis* Borkh. (Alder Kitten)
  Larva on sallow at Thorington, August 1841 (*Entomologist*, 1:226).
*Gluphisia crenata* Esp. (Dusky Marbled Brown)
  Ongar Park Wood, a female in June 1839 and another in June 1841
  (*Entomologist*, 1:156).
*Notodonta tritophus* Schiff. (Three-humped Prominent)
  Bred on 10 August 1842 from a larva found on aspen at St. Osyth
  (VCH).
*Dasychira fascelina* L. (Dark Tussock)
  Between Colchester and Marks Tey and at Great Bentley (VCH);
  Woodham Walter prior to 1882 (*Essex Field Club Trans.*, 3:40);
  near Leigh-on-Sea, last seen *c.* 1876 in a locality since built over
  (*per* HCH).
(*Setina irrorella* L. (Dew Footman)
  A report of larvae on Mersea Island and at St. Osyth 'many years'
  ago was thought to have been a case of mistaken identity (VCH).)
*Heterogenea asella* Schiff. (Triangle)
  Widely distributed in the Epping Forest district; singly at Colches-
  ter and Little Bentley (VCH).
*Sciapteron tabaniformis* Rott. (Dusky Clearwing)
  Epping, 1839 (VCH); specimen bred, 1912 (*London Nat.*, 33:146).
*Aegeria spheciformis* Schiff. (White-barred Clearwing)
  'South Essex', 1888 and 1890 (VCH); Brentwood, a number, 1895
  (*Entomologist*, 44:158); Thorndon Park, 1903 (*Ent. Rec.*, 16:23).
*Aegeria chrysidiformis* Esp. (Fiery Clearwing)
  Near Southend-on-Sea up to 1860 (VCH).

*Euxoa cursoria* Hufn. (Coast Dart)

Occasionally at Harwich, Walton-on-the-Naze, Clacton-on-Sea and St. Osyth (VCH). This is one of the most surprising omissions from the main list: the species may well await rediscovery on north-east Essex shingle beaches.

(*Agrotis crassa* Hübn. (Great Dart)

This species was said to have been taken at Epping in June/July 1841 (*Entomologist*, 1:155). The occurrence is not mentioned in the VCH.)

*Actebia praecox* L. (Portland Dart)

Once at rest in a house at Colchester and once in the larval state near Clacton-on-Sea (VCH).

*Anarta myrtilli* L. (Beautiful Yellow Underwing)

Tiptree Heath (VCH); Danbury (*Essex Field Club Trans.*, 3:47).

*Hadena contigua* Schiff. (Beautiful Brocade)

Dedham up to 1890 (VCH).

*Hadena dysodea* Schiff. (Small Ranunculus)

Formerly very common, latterly scarce, in the Coggeshall district where the larvae fed on cultivated lettuce; also recorded at Colchester and, on *Lactuca virosa* (Wild Lettuce), at Walton-on-the-Naze (VCH).

The species seems to have disappeared from Essex in 1918, when the last specimens were noted in the Colchester area. After that date it was regarded as extinct in the British Isles until the mid-1930s when examples occurred in Somerset and Hertfordshire. C. G. Barrett wrote in 1897 in *The Lepidoptera of the British Isles* that caterpillars of *H. dysodea* fed on the blossoms and seed heads of lettuce. Apparently the larvae were regarded as a pest in seed-growing districts and were particularly plentiful in the late 1890s in parts of Cambridgeshire. R. F. Bretherton, in his paper on lost British butterflies and moths (*Ent. Gaz.*, 2: 211–240), wrote that it looked as if, after contraction of its natural range in the last quarter of the 19th century, *H. dysodea* was overtaken by a sudden disaster in its main strongholds in Essex, Cambridgeshire and other eastern counties about 1900. The species failed to recover from this set-back. Three specimens were taken at light at Berkhampsted, Herts., in June 1936 and another was caught in the same locality in 1937. Bretherton considered this to be evidence that this attractive moth had survived in isolated pockets. The species remains reasonably common in France and Belgium so it is fair to assume that its disappearance from Essex was due to a combination of climatic factors and changes in horticultural practice. Lettuce is no longer grown for seed at Kelvedon and Coggeshall except in very small patches.

*Xylomyges conspicillaris* L. (Silver Cloud)

Danbury, June 1873 (*Entomologist*, 6:427); near Brentwood, May 1877 (*Entomologist*, 10:255).

(*Caradrina superstes* Ochs. (Powdered Fulvous)
Said to have been taken near Brentwood on 18 July 1890 (*Ent. Rec.*, 1:335).)

*Trachea atriplicis* L. (Orache Brocade)
The VCH merely says 'given as an Essex species in Newman's *British Moths*', but it is probable that it was once thinly spread over the county. The last British example but one was taken by the late F. J. Hanbury at Burnham-on-Crouch in July 1911, but he did not record it for obvious reasons. The latter specimen passed to the collection of the late E. S. A. Baynes and then to HCH who still has it.

(*Apamea furva* Schiff. (Confused Brindle)
Alleged to have been taken at Epping in June/July 1841 and May 1842 (*Entomologist*, 1:155, 374).)

(*Cucullia gnaphalii* Hübn. (Cudweed Shark)
Given, without locality, as an Essex species by C. G. Barrett in the last century (*The Lepidoptera of the British Isles*, first edition, 2: 42).)

*Lithophane socia* Hufn. (Pale Pinion)
Taken at Temple Mills, Leyton (VCH).

*Emmelia trabealis* Scop. (Spotted Sulphur)
Taken at Temple Mills, Leyton (VCH), and near Hackney Marshes (*London Nat.*, 35:66). The species was introduced at Mucking by CRNB *c.* 1900 but survived only for two years (*per* HCH).

*Catocala promissa* Schiff. (Light Crimson Underwing)
Larva beaten from oak in Lodge Wood, Langham (VCH).

*Catephia alchymista* Schiff. (Alchymist)
One at rest on oak trunk near Colchester, 9 June 1875 (VCH).

*Bomolocha fontis* Thunb. (Beautiful Snout)
Feering Bury, Kelvedon, May/June 1916 (*Entomologist*, 49:190).

*Scopula rubiginata* Hufn. (Tawny Wave)
Epping Forest, not uncommon, 1869–74 (Prof. R. Meldola; *Essex Nat. Mag.*, 168).

*Sterrha dilutaria* Hübn. (Silky Wave)
Southend-on-Sea, July 1892 (*Ent. Rec.*, 3:232); July 1894 (*Ent. Rec.*, 5:228).

(*Lythria purpuraria* L. (Purple-barred Yellow Carpet)
Three specimens were said to have been taken in Essex in or before 1869 (*Entomologist*, 4:352).)

*Colostygia olivata* Schiff. (Beech Green Carpet)
Epping Forest, occasional, 1869–74 (Prof. R. Meldola; *Essex Nat. Mag.*, 167).

*Pareulype berberata* Schiff. (Barberry Carpet)
Plentiful in Saffron Walden district; formerly found at Epping (VCH); near Chelmsford, June 1846 (*Zoologist*, 5:1661).

*Thera firmata* Hübn. (Reddish Pine Carpet)
Birch and Berechurch; also taken 'rather freely' by CRNB (VCH).

The last-named operated in the Mucking area of Thames-side.

*Hydriomena ruberata* Freyer (Ruddy Highflyer)
    Occurred sparingly at Colchester (VCH).

*Rheumaptera hastata* L. (Argent and Sable)
    Epping Forest, plentiful in 1846 (*Essex Nat.*, 1:111); Southend-on-
    Sea, Brentwood, Messing and St. Osyth (VCH); Childerditch,
    common, some years prior to 1939 (the late R. G. Williment *per*
    EFW). It is possible, although perhaps unlikely, that the latter is a
    post-1925 record.

*Odezia atrata* L. (Chimney Sweeper)
    Epping Forest, 1893 (*Essex Nat.,* 7:127); Hainault (VCH).

*Trichopteryx polycommata* Schiff. (Barred Tooth-striped)
    Epping, in or prior to 1836 (VCH).

*Ortholitha mucronata* Scop. (Common Lead-belle)
    The only Essex records of this species come from the Epping
    Forest district, viz., Loughton, 25 May 1895 and 23 June 1908
    (E. Gardner coll.); 27 May 1911 (2) (*London Nat.*, 36:85); Epping
    Forest, undated (E. Gardner coll.).

*Discoloxia blomeri* Curt. (Blomer's Rivulet)
    Once taken at Wanstead, presumably a wanderer from outside the
    county (VCH).

*Anticollix sparsata* Treits. (Dentated Pug)
    Once in Epping Forest (*London Nat.*, 37:148). This was almost
    certainly taken in the present century but the date is unknown.

*Eupithecia pini* Retz. (Cloaked Pug)
    Highams Park, 1892; Harwich (VCH).

*Eupithecia irriguata* Hübn. (Marbled Pug)
    Formerly found at Epping (VCH).

*Eupithecia pygmaeata* Hübn. (Marsh Pug)
    Leyton, one, between 1869 and 1874 (Prof. R. Meldola; *Essex Nat.
    Mag.*, 167).

*Eupithecia denotata* Hübn. (Campanula or Bell-flower Pug)
    Leyton, 1–2 between 1869 and 1874 (Prof. R. Meldola; *Essex Nat.
    Mag.*, 167).

(*Eupithecia egenaria* H.-S. (Pauper Pug)
    Said by the VCH to have been taken at Loughton, but early records
    of this species, which has only recently been admitted to the
    British List, are treated with great reserve.)

*Cepphis advenaria* Hübn. (Little Thorn)
    Formerly rare at Eastwood near Southend in a locality long
    since built over (VCH); Epping Forest, June 1892 (*Ent. Rec.*,
    3:179).

*Cleora cinctaria* Schiff. (Ringed Carpet or Beauty)
    Epping and Ongar (VCH).

*Deileptenia ribeata* Clerck (Satin Beauty)
    Epping and Ongar (VCH).

*Pachycnemia hippocastanaria* Hübn. (Horse-chestnut)

J. F. Stephens (*Illustrations of British Entomology*, 1828–36) stated that he possessed 'two fine specimens' from Rochford.

*Isturgia limbaria* F. (Frosted Yellow)

The VCH stated that it was formerly fairly common along the railway embankment and cuttings between Lexden and Stanway, near Colchester, but had been exterminated as a result of the firing of the herbage. This insect, now extinct in Britain, was not uncommon in restricted areas of east Suffolk where broom grew extensively but finally disappeared after much destruction of its foodplant in 1903. Edward Platten, one of the last to see this pretty little insect in its Suffolk haunts, wrote a long paper on its history in the Suffolk Naturalists' Society *Transactions* (2 (PT. 1): 5–10) in which he refers to *limbaria* having been discovered commonly at Colchester (i.e., the above-mentioned site) by W. H. Harwood in 1868. Harwood took it at Colchester again in 1869. Platten also wrote: 'Gill found it near Grays in that county (Essex) during August (1869)': this could have been an offshoot of an extremely localised colony in north Kent to which Platten referred in his paper and which was said to have vanished in the 1860s. After that there is no further reference to Essex in the literature apart from a claim that it was taken 'somewhere in Essex' in 1913 by C. N. Hughes, but it is now known that specimens (whether the same as those last mentioned we do not know) were taken in the Kelvedon district by the late P. C. Reid in 1913 and 1914 (J. W. Corder *per* HCH).

*Idaea lineata* Scop. (Black-veined Looper)

Found freely on the downs at Leigh-on-Sea prior to 1860 (VCH).

*Aspitates gilvaria* Schiff. (Straw Belle)

Southend-on-Sea (VCH).

# List of Contributors

Rev. D. J. L. Agassiz
P. B. M. Allan*
P. F. Allfrey
Dr. M. E. Anthoney
D. A. Ashwell*

P. Betts
Biological Records
  Centre, Nature
  Conservancy Council
Bishop's Stortford
  Natural History
  Society
A. D. Blaxill
R. Blindell
R. F. Bretherton
R. W. Brewster
F. D. Buck
Rev. C. R. N. Burrows
J. F. Burton

J. Chainey
J. A. Challis
H. E. Chipperfield
Colchester and District
  Natural History Society
C. S. Colman*
R. R. Cook
W. L. Coster
C. E. Coulson
J. E. Cowley
D. Cox
C. Craufurd*

G. C. Davidson
Mrs. F. Davis
G. Dent
A. J. Dewick
S. F. J. Dewick
D. G. Down
R. J. Drane
C. Dunster

H. F. D. Elder

L. S. Ellis
Lt. Col. A. M. Emmet
N. Endacott
Essex Naturalists' Trust

J. L. Fielding
J. Firmin
J. B. Fisher
P. C. Follett
P. French
J. T. Friedlein

G. Glombek
Mrs. R. Green
K. W. Grimwood

B. Harley
Mrs. C. Harrison
Brig. G. F. Heaney
J. Heath
Dr. R. C. Hider
S. Hudgell
H. C. Huggins
B. P. Hutchins

Miss A. Impey

P. Jennings

Dr. H. B. D. Kettlewell

S. E. Linsell

Col. C. G. Mangles
R. Marsh
Paymaster-in-Chief
  G. F. Mathew, R.N.
  (Ret'd)
C. Mellows*
R. K. Merrifield
M. R. S. Mitchell
D. More
F. B. Murray

G. T. Nunn

J. Pearce
B. W. J. Perkins
D. Pryor
G. A. Pyman
T. A. Pyman

J. Reid
R. J. Revell
C. P. Rose
I. C. Rose
Rothamsted
  Experimental Station

C. W. Saunders
W. K. Seabrook
W. P. Seabrook
G. H. B. Sell
I. Sims
B. Skinner
J. T. Smith
R. Smith
R. A. Softly
L. T. Staines
G. Summers

M. L. Tasker
Dr. M. Thain
R. Tomlinson
Dr. D. C. Twinn

Mrs. R. Upton

V. Veal

M. F. Walker (and
  Felsted School Natural
  History Society)
P. J. Wanstall (assisted
  by G. Skinner)
J. K. Weston
E. F. Williams
Dr. C. G. M. de Worms
Writtle Agricultural
  College

* West Essex records attributed to those so marked have been extracted from the List of Lepidoptera contained in the *Transactions* of the Bishop's Stortford and District Natural History Society, Vol. I, Part I.

The bulk of H. C. Huggins's South Essex records are also to be found in the *South Essex Naturalist*: 21st Anniversary Number, 1934/1955.

# References Consulted in the Preparation of the Systematic List

Barrett, C. G. (1893–1907). *The Lepidoptera of the British Isles*. London.
Harwood, W. H. (1903). Lepidoptera, *Victoria County History of Essex*. London.
Newman, E. (1869). *Illustrated Natural History of British Moths*. London.
Newman, E. (1871). *Natural History of British Butterflies*. London.
South, R. (1907). *The Moths of the British Isles* (1961 Ed.). London.
Stephens, J. H. (1828–34). *Illustrations of British Entomology*.
de Worms, Dr. C. G. M. (1949). The Butterflies of London and its Surroundings, *London Naturalist*, 29.
de Worms, Dr. C. G. M. (1953–59). The Moths of London and its Surroundings, *London Naturalist*, 33–39.

Bishop's Stortford and District Natural History Society: *Transactions*, Vol. I, Part I: List of Lepidoptera.
*British Birds*.
British (formerly South London) Entomological and Natural History Society: *Proceedings*.
Colchester and District Natural History Society: *Annual Reports*.
*Countryside*.
The Royal Entomological Society of London: *Proceedings and Transactions*.
*The Entomologist*.
*The Entomologist's Gazette*.
*The Entomologist's Monthly Magazine*.
*The Entomologist's Record and Journal of Variation*.
*The Entomologist's Weekly Intelligencer*.
The Epping Forest and County of Essex Naturalists' Field Club (subsequently Essex Field Club): *Transactions*.
*The Essex Naturalist*.
*The London Naturalist*.
*South Essex Naturalist*, 21st Anniversary Number, 1934/1955.
Suffolk Naturalists' Society: *Transactions*.
*The Zoologist*.

# Index

Scientific and English names of Species of Lepidoptera named in the Systematic List and its Appendix.

141

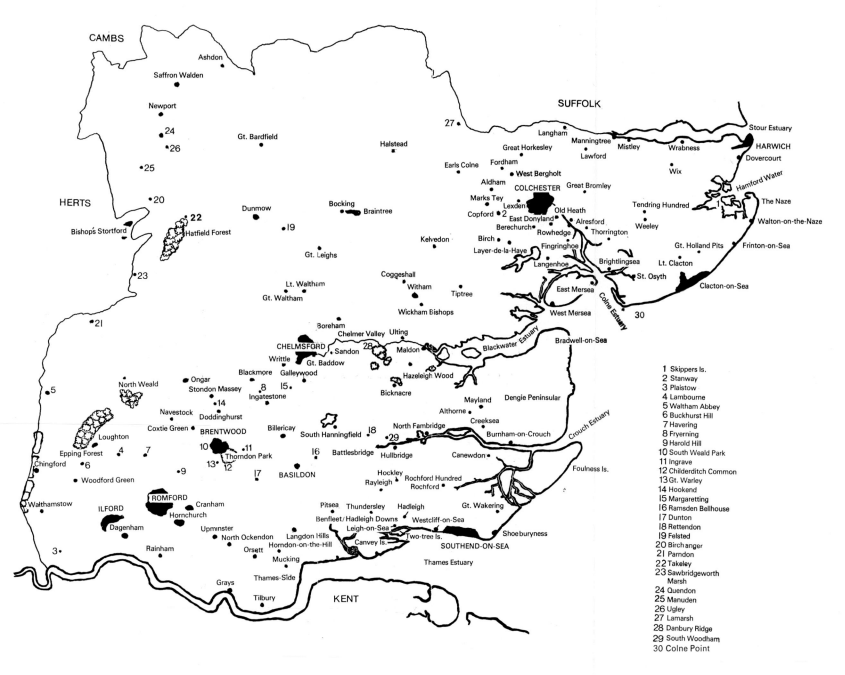

# MAP of ESSEX

CAMBS

Ashdon

Saffron Walden

Newport

•24

•26

•25

•20

HERTS

Bishop's Stortford

Gt. Bardfield

Halstead

SUFFOLK

27•

Langham

Manningtree

Mistley

Wrabness

Stour Estuary

HARWICH

Dovercourt

Great Horkesley

Lawford

Earls Colne

Fordham

West Bergholt

Wix

Hamford Water

Aldham

COLCHESTER

Great Bromley

Marks Tey

Lexden

Old Heath

Tendring Hundred

The Naze

Copford

•2

East Donyland

Alresford

Walton-on-the-Naze

Dunmow

Bocking

Braintree

Berechurch

Rowhedge

Thorrington

Weeley

1

**22**

Hatfield Forest

•19

Kelvedon

Birch

Fingringhoe

Gt. Holland Pits

Frinton-on-Sea

Layer-de-la-Haye

Langenhoe

Brightlingsea

Lt. Clacton

•23

Gt. Leighs

Coggeshall

Witham

Tiptree

East Mersea

St. Osyth

Clacton-on-Sea

•21

Lt. Waltham

Wickham Bishops

West Mersea

Colne Estuary

30

Gt. Waltham

Boreham

Chelmer Valley

Ulting

Blackwater Estuary

Bradwell-on-Sea

CHELMSFORD

Sandon

28

Maldon

Writtle

Gt. Baddow

North Weald

Ongar

Blackmore

Galleywood

Hazeleigh Wood

Dengie Peninsular

•5

Stondon Massey

8

15

Bicknacre

Mayland

Navestock

•14

Ingatestone

Althorne

Creeksea

Crouch Estuary

Loughton

Coxtie Green

Doddinghurst

Billericay

South Hanningfield

•18

North Fambridge

Burnham-on-Crouch

Epping Forest

BRENTWOOD

10

•11

16

Battlesbridge

•29

Canewdon

Foulness Is.

Chingford

•6

•4

7

13•

12

Thorndon Park

Hullbridge

Gt. Wakering

•9

•17

BASILDON

Hockley

Rochford Hundred

Walthamstow

Woodford Green

Rayleigh

Rochford

ILFORD

ROMFORD

Cranham

Pitsea

Thundersley

Hadleigh

Gt. Wakering

Hornchurch

Benfleet/Hadleigh Downs

Westcliff-on-Sea

Dagenham

Upminster

Leigh-on-Sea

3•

North Ockendon

Langdon Hills

Two-tree Is.

Shoeburyness

Rainham

Orsett

Horndon-on-the-Hill

Canvey Is.

SOUTHEND-ON-SEA

Mucking

Thames-Side

Thames Estuary

Grays

Tilbury

KENT

1 Skippers Is.
2 Stanway
3 Plaistow
4 Lambourne
5 Waltham Abbey
6 Buckhurst Hill
7 Havering
8 Fryerning
9 Harold Hill
10 South Weald Park
11 Ingrave
12 Childerditch Common
13 Gt. Warley
14 Hookend
15 Margaretting
16 Ramsden Bellhouse
17 Dunton
18 Rettendon
19 Felsted
20 Birch anger
21 Parndon
22 Takeley
23 Sawbridgeworth
   Marsh
24 Quendon
25 Manuden
26 Ugley
27 Lamarsh
28 Danbury Ridge
29 South Woodham
30 Colne Point